Mass Listeria

Mass Listeria
The Meaning of Health Scares

Theodore Dalrymple

André Deutsch

First published in Great Britain in 1998 by
André Deutsch Ltd,
76 Dean Street,
London W1V 5HA

André Deutsch is a subsidiary of VCI plc

A catalogue record for this title is available from
the British Library

ISBN 0 233 99137 9

Typeset by Derek Doyle & Associates
Mold, Flintshire
Printed and bound by St Edmundsbury Press,
Suffolk

Several physicians and research scientists have helped me in the writing of *Mass Listeria*, but as it is unlikely that an association with a work of this nature will add to their public standing, I prefer to thank them while preserving their anonymity.

. . . no man ever understands quite his own artful dodges to escape from the grim shadow of self-knowledge.

Joseph Conrad, *Lord Jim*

I

Man is born immortal, but everywhere he dies.

At the end of the twentieth century, death is an anomaly which requires an explanation. Worse than an anomaly, it is an injustice. So, indeed, is illness: for not only are illnesses unevenly distributed across the population, but they strike without regard to the virtue of the victim. Many an alcoholic has protested to me, when I have apprised him of the parlous state of his liver, that he knows of people who drink far more than he and yet are in the most perfect of hepatic health.* In vain do I insist that Nature is not a court of justice, and that what is the case is the case, regardless of just deserts. The belief is now general that Man has achieved such mastery over Nature that, if life turns out to be unfair, as it always does, human malevolence must be to blame. Death these days is definitely somebody's fault.

And so we have come full circle, back to the belief of the Azande, the Sudanese tribe described by Evans-Pritchard in the 1920s, that no death occurs without witchcraft:

---

* When an eminent epidemiologist died of lung cancer, his obituarist in the *International Journal of Epidemiology* felt constrained to point out that he did so despite never having smoked: in other words, he died as an innocent, undeservedly. Moreover, the world had not lost, but had been robbed of, a great man. The Spanish Inquisition itself could not have behaved more unjustly than brute reality.

though nowadays negligence has taken the all-pervasive role of witchcraft in the human imagination. If grandmama died at the early age of eighty-six, surely there must have been some error of omission or commission on the part of the doctors to explain it? When men are responsible for everything, even the existence of death, there is no room for sadness, only for bitterness. Besides, when nothing happens by chance or accident there is always the prospect, however remote, of compensation. Money does not help you to mourn, but it does allow you to resent in comfort.

The natural state of Man is not only to be alive, but to be healthy. And everyone has the right to a healthy life – the Universal Declaration of Human Rights as good as says so. Illness, or any deviation from bodily perfection, is thus experienced as an infringement of one's entitlements. And health, as the constitution of the World Health Organisation defines it, is not merely the absence of disease, but the presence of complete physical, social and psychological well-being. It follows that all human activity whatsoever is a matter of health, and therefore that anything which causes distress is both a threat to health and an infringement of human rights. It also means that the World Health Organisation is unlikely to work itself out of a job in the near future.

Of course, no one is ever entirely healthy: at least, not in the World Health Organisation's sense of the word. But having one's rights infringed has its compensations. In the first place, it lends one a certain importance. Only someone who is worth something can be denied his due; and therefore if we are not getting our due, we must be worth something. The injustice done us assures us of our significance in the order of things.

Second, resentment brings its own sour joys and satisfactions. We are the moral superiors at least of the people who deny us the thing to which we are entitled. It would, after all, be far worse to live in a world in which no one denied us anything, and yet in which we still felt disgruntled. We might then feel compelled to look inward, always a painful experience, for lack of anywhere else to look.

To be denied the health to which one is entitled is not a minor matter. The cover of a recent edition of a magazine for travellers on the German railways put it very succinctly: 'Health, the Highest Good'. In other words, we should not value health in order that we may do the things we wish to do without physical impediment or discomfort, but on the contrary, all that we do should have as its sole object the achievement and preservation of good health. For the purpose of life is to live longer, and to be denied health is to be denied purpose.

The fundamentally democratic, equitable and egalitarian rule of human existence hitherto – namely, one man, one death – is no longer accepted without question. American publications, reporting on one dread disease or other, refer to the numbers of *Americans* who die from it every year, usually in a tone which suggests that it is an outrage, or at least an anachronism, that Americans should die at all, let alone of this particular disease. An American death is not like any other, but is uniquely tragic, regrettable and reprehensible (seeking guidance on what he might include in the Stop Press of the *New York Times*, a young journalist was given the following rule of thumb: one American death equals five British deaths, which equal ten thousand Chinese deaths). That Americans should still die when every contrivance of technology is available to them can only mean that someone, somewhere, is not doing his job properly. Abolitionists in America do not seek to abolish the death penalty: they seek to abolish death itself.

The search for health – that is to say, the recovery of Man's natural state of immortality – imposes certain burdens not only upon society and its supreme incarnation, the government, but upon each of us as individuals. If we have a right to health, we have a duty to live healthily. On a recent journey to South America, my wife bought a magazine called *Health and Fitness* at the airport news-stand to read on the aeroplane. (That the modern obsession with health is now truly worldwide is illustrated by the fact that, at the bookstall in Caracas airport, half the books on display concerned health, including *Paz, Amor y Autocuración – Peace, Love and Self-Healing –* and *Sanar es Viajar – To Heal is to Voyage*; and by the fact that the first newspaper I opened in Colombia advertised promi-nently machines by means of which hypochondriacs might take and record their blood pressure more or less continu-ously, day and night. Not, one would have supposed, the first instrument of self-preservation in such a country for those with more money than they could spend.)

I leafed through *Health and Fitness*, which on its cover claimed to be 'All you need for life' – the kind of extreme claim more usually made by fundamentalist Christians or Moslems with regard to the Bible or the Koran. It contained articles extolling this month's elixirs of life: cranberries for infection of the urinary tract, cold Earl Grey tea for cold sores, turmeric for colitis, asthma and psoriasis. The promise was implicitly held out that, if only you were to eat the right things in the right quantities and combinations, you too would first become, and then remain, like the slen-der but strong-limbed young women with perfect complex-ions who pullulate in these pages, happiness shining from their pearly teeth, smiling with the bliss of eternal youth.

Ageing occurs – hair falls out, wrinkles develop – because people drink beer and eat the wrong things.

But the *locus classicus* within the magazine of the idea of health as the highest of highest goods occurred in an interview on the last page with a woman called Karen Voight, who is described as 'an aerobics diva'. The interview was entitled 'My body, my life', which suggests at the very least that the perfection of her body was the whole purpose of her existence; and a photograph shows her resting, supple and shapely of limb, against a marble column. She wears that deadening nothing-you-can-say-will-knock-me-off-my-perch smile which evangelical Christians, who know that God loves them, are inclined to wear to demonstrate that they are happy: a happiness which is, for them, both a consequence and a proof of God's love for them. The mask must not slip for a moment, or its essential falseness and theatricality becomes apparent to all, including the person wearing it.

The photograph of Karen Voight is taken at a tactful distance from her because, though fit, she is clearly not in the first flush of youth, and a close-up might reveal a blemish or two, a few of Time's ravishes, which it is the ultimate purpose of aerobics to banish, and would thus rather dash the promise of eternal youth which the interview holds out to those who follow the diva's advice and example.

The interviewer is clearly in awe of her subject, for the tone of the questioning is obsequious. Karen Voight is to aerobics what Newton was to physics or Darwin to biology.

How does it feel, the diva is asked, to have one of the most coveted bodies in the [fitness] industry?

'It feels good that people recognise what I've achieved. But I didn't do it for that reason . . . I've also sacrificed a lot for it – I worked out seven days a week for fifteen years;

gave up partying and late nights; ate healthily and worked out while I was travelling.'

One is reminded of those holy men who wore filthy rags, drank wormwood and gall, licked the suppurating wounds of the poor, and slept for many years bolt upright in a cell no bigger than a coffin, the sooner and surer to gain that blissful eternal life in which, presumably, such revolting exercises would no longer be necessary.

But what in this post-religious and secular world of ours could motivate someone to such mortification of the flesh?

'The fact that I like how I feel – it gives me confidence and self-esteem.'

Never, one might suppose, was narcissistic complacency more dearly or more strenuously bought; but these are not the only advantages which her labours of Hercules (or Sisyphus) have brought her. Asked what is the best thing about being fit, *la diva* replies, 'My energy levels and endurance.'

In other words, the purpose of exercising seven days a week for fifteen years is so that you can continue to exercise seven days a week. But this is not all, far from it. 'I don't get sick or have problems you need to see a doctor for.'

With as much reason and justice might an entirely sedentary man who never visits his doctor attribute his exceptional good health to his physical inactivity ('I never do anything which could injure me'), though he would be most unlikely to suppose that, if only he kept inactive enough, he would never ever require the services of a doctor. For although Miss Voight exercises sixteen times a week in all – three bicycle workouts, followed by seven abdominals and stretches, three hi-los, and three sculpt and defines, to use her own technical terminology – she will in the end have a fatal illness requiring medical attention, and would do so even if she were to increase her sessions to, say, twenty-five a week. Pride goeth before destruction, and a macrobiotic diet before a fall.

Although in general *la diva* is content with her lot, being happy with her body, because 'I think everyone has to accept what they have as part of what they are', she readily admits to one terrible imperfection when asked directly whether she has any vices. 'Yes – coffee.'

One thinks of poor, sinning Dr Chasuble and his susceptibility to colds. But what in Oscar Wilde is a good-natured and mildly satirical joke is here uttered in deadly earnest. The remark allows us to enter the moral world of the health-and-exercise fanatic: a world as full of moral hazards as the London streets were for Victorian girls of a certain class.

If drinking coffee is the nearest she comes to a vice, then refraining from drinking it is the nearest she comes to virtue. The world being full of snares and delusions, such as chocolate and fried potatoes, she can achieve a really sublime level of virtue by denying herself the thousand little treats that flesh is heir to, while remaining self-absorbed and egocentric to a quite grotesque degree. Indeed, on *la diva*'s evidence, virtue seems actively to require such self-absorption; and sin, in her philosophy, is transmuted into *lèse-santé*. Everything which is harmful to health is forbidden while everything which is good for it is compulsory.

Lest anyone suppose that in selecting this Maria Callas of callisthenics I have deliberately selected a freak, a nonentity of no cultural significance, I feel I should point out that Karen Voight was once voted 'The Most Successful Working Woman in the United States', and that her views are therefore by no means considered outrageous or silly.

About a fifth of my patients in their twenties say that 'Keep fit' is their only interest.

'Fit for what?' I ask, a question which usually nonplusses them, when it does not produce acute existential panic.

This is not surprising. If health is the highest good, it doesn't make sense to ask why you should pursue health to the exclusion of everything else. You don't, after all, ask a desert hermit why he wants to achieve grace in the eyes of God. And so, in every Western city, there are scores of fitness centres, in which on every night of the year thousands of people take voluntarily to the treadmill, pedalling furiously on bicycles which don't move, the expression on their faces a mixture of pain, determination, boredom and complacency that they are doing good works.

II

If remaining healthy imposes responsibilities upon individuals, they pale into insignificance by comparison with those which devolve upon governments. This is because only governments can be expected to deal with the hazards to health which lurk unseen everywhere, especially in this polluted world of ours, in which foul chemicals assault us by land, sea, air and food. Is it not the case that our way of life is uniquely distant from that which Nature intended for Man, and therefore uniquely unhealthy?

No man can be expected to be his own toxicologist: he must rely upon the authorities to carry out the relevant tests and make the world safe for him. And if the authorities should fail to do so they are negligent in the discharge of their duties, or – which is more likely – they are in the pay of the giant profit-seeking and profit-maximising companies responsible for the pollution in the first place.

That the world is full of hazards is, of course, axiomatic. Cursed are they that have not seen and yet believe, for they shall live in perpetual anxiety. But they shall also receive the benefits of incipient paranoia; for though the world of the paranoid is frightening and full of danger, it is not meaningless or conducted without reference to his estimable person, as is the world of the man who believes that the world is ruled by accident, chance and blind indifference. The man who sits in his lonely lodging, fearing to venture forth in his belief that there is a vast conspiracy afoot, the principal target of whose malevolence is himself, is not more to be pitied than the man who sits in his lonely lodging not venturing forth from lack of friends with whom to associate. A conspiracy against oneself often gives meaning to a life previously regarded as a meaningless chapter of accidents.

Do we not read in our newspapers and hear on our radios of new and previously unsuspected hazards every day? A rabid bat has bitten a pregnant woman, who has to undergo emergency immunisation: beware of flying mammals. Mobile telephones may cause brain tumours among frequent users: cut short your telephone calls. Grapefruit juice may interfere with the metabolism of certain drugs, leading to potentially fatal overdosage: consult a doctor before drinking. Conservatives, reacting against the fashion for subjecting every institution and idea to the scathing mockery of satirists, are wont to cry, 'Is nothing sacred?' Healthists – those who believe that health is the highest good – are wont to cry, 'Is anything safe?' – to which the answer, of course, is 'No'.

Modern hypochondriasis is orientated towards the future rather than to the present: there are no symptoms at the moment, but they might – or will – develop in a few years' or decades' time. Traditional hypochondriasis, by contrast, was sustained by the twinges felt in the here and now, and by the belief that the slightest variations in the pulse rate or the colour of the urine or the frequency and consistency of the bowel motion heralded grave illness which required immediate treatment if a fatal outcome was to be avoided. Old-fashioned hypochondriacs could be easily placated or fobbed off, at least for a short time, with impressive pink placebos; but the anxieties of the modern hypochondriac are not so easily disposed of.

It is hardly surprising that, in an age of medical miracles, hypochondriasis should itself have been turned into an illness or disease (Somatization Disorder, according to the *Diagnostic and Statistical Manual*, third revised edition, of the American Psychiatric Association) rather than a condition of the human soul. To worry about diseases you don't have is itself a disease, so you do have a disease after all, and researchers have tried to elucidate the risk factors for developing it. This suggests the intriguing possibility of what theorists might call metahypochondriasis, in which the sufferer will not worry about illness present or to come, but will worry instead about becoming worried about them.

'Doctor, I'm worried that I may be becoming a hypochondriac. I have many of the risk factors for it – my mother and her mother before her were hypochondriacs.'

In a world so full of hazards that substances which we have been thoughtlessly consuming for years (coffee, for example, or salt) may yet turn out to be the principal undercover agent of the Grim Reaper, it is likely that not only will worrying about imaginary illnesses be counted an illness, but *not* worrying about them will be likewise counted an illness – Denial Disorder, perhaps. Delusions of health will afflict not only those who feel well at the present moment, but those who fail to recognise the dangers by which they are surrounded, and who stubbornly fail to accept the evidence published daily in the newspapers and broadcast daily on the television and radio that they are beset by a host of hidden enemies. Their delusions of well-being will have serious consequences for their health, and thus count as a true illness; for will they not refuse to take the selenium (or zirconium) supplements which have been conclusively demonstrated this week to prevent the development of heart attacks, rheumatoid arthritis and polyarteritis nodosa?

However, abandoning to individuals the task of taking precautions for themselves is insufficient. A few years ago a friend of mine was visited for the weekend by some relatives known to be what health educationists call *proactive* in matters of their own health. They appeared in tin helmets, to deflect the electromagnetic radiation which they were convinced was leaking, *à la* Thurber's aunt, from my friend's household plugs, and which would wreak havoc with the delicate machinery of their brains. They upbraided him for his casual dismissal of the dangers and accused him virtually of child abuse, inasmuch as he gave no helmets to his children to protect them from the insidious radiation. They came prepared with a sheaf of papers to prove the dangers (leukaemia among them), and proceeded to stuff the sockets with aluminium foil, in the process causing a small fire which might have burnt the house down.

Surely, if the hazards of ordinary household electric sockets are what they are claimed by some activists to be, it is the duty of the government to rewire the entire country with safer fitments or, if such are not available, to provide everyone with radiation-deflecting helmets, the wearing of which indoors would naturally enough be made compulsory? If health is the highest good, it is worth suffering some minor inconveniences or infringements of liberty to attain and preserve it.

The consumption of common salt, as we now know, is associated with a rise in blood pressure. A rise in blood pressure increases the risk of stroke, one of the biggest killers and incapacitators in Western society. It follows (does it not?) that if the population were to reduce its consumption of this deadly substance, it would live longer, though perhaps not for ever since there are so many other hazards about.

You might have supposed that it would be sufficient to inform the public of the alleged (but not universally agreed) dangers of salt and leave it to decide what to do about it, if anything: whether to eat or to abstain from salty foods. But you would be wrong to suppose any such thing. A powerful campaign is gathering force among the epidemiologists and their publicists, the editors of the principal medical journals, which is bound to be successful in the end, to force the government to change our diet for the 'better' whether we like it or not, via legislation to force food companies to reduce the salt content of their products and so forth.

The justification for this incipient interference is as

follows: salt is bad for you, and a large proportion of your overall consumption of it is derived from the prepared foods which are an integral part of the modern diet. The food companies put more salt in their products than is strictly necessary for purely preservative purposes, to make them more attractive and tastier to a population already accustomed to a high salt intake. But this avidity for salt is culturally, not physiologically, determined; and a man who has either never eaten salty food, or has eaten it in the past but has for some reason grown unaccustomed to it, finds it unattractive. Salt is an acquired taste which can also be lost.

So while the adjustment to foods with a lower salt content might cause some initial discontent (distress would be too strong a word), we should all get used to, and even come to like, eating a low salt diet before very long, and to the extent that we were then less susceptible to stroke we should all be better off.

Stroke having been vanquished by these means, we should live (on average) three months longer – let us say. But we should still, alas, die of *something*. The epidemiologists would be sure to discover a dietary association with whatever disease now killed us instead of stroke: because all flesh is grass, all illness is likewise grass. And as the whirligig of epidemiological research brings in its revenges, it is not at all unlikely that the new killer disease will be found to be associated with a diet low in sodium chloride. Indeed, one of the first patients I treated after qualification illustrated to perfection the endless cycle of epidemiological fashion. He suffered from diverticulitis, an inflammation of the appendix-like pouches which sometimes develop in the wall of the colon. Many years previously he had been enjoined by his specialist assiduously to avoid all foods which might add bulk to his stool: the wall of his large bowel couldn't take the strain, apparently. I, however, was of the first generation of doctors which had taken the late Sir Dennis Burkitt's theories to heart. This surgeon, a man of the utmost integrity, had worked in East and Central Africa, where he had noticed the rarity with which the otherwise unhealthy populations of those regions developed certain diseases – later included among the 'diseases of civilisation', those being still the days when the word civilisation could be used without the ironical twist it is usually given today. Among those diseases were appendicitis, haemorrhoids, varicose veins, bowel cancer and diverticulitis. Sir Dennis attributed the relative health of the African large bowel, give or take a bout of amoebic dysentery and more lately cholera, to the huge, indeed elephantine, bulk of the stool, and also its frequency (up to three times a day), which in turn he attributed to a diet high in non-absorbable and unrefined fibrous vegetable matter, eaten – it must be said – from necessity rather than from choice.

Not being intellectually rebellious by nature, I believed implicitly what Sir Dennis said, and enjoined my patient to alter his diet once more in favour of foods which would bulk his stool. Not surprisingly, perhaps, my patient responded with a modern equivalent of Macbeth's exclamation, 'Throw physic to the dogs, I'll none of it.' He said that henceforth he would eat whatever he liked, and in all probability he has paid for his rashness with his life: for he was over seventy then, and this was more than twenty years ago.

Sir Dennis, incidentally, became a world-famous apostle of bulk. The number of diseases ascribed to a deficiency of fibre in the diet grew, if not exponentially, at least very substantially, and came to include both diabetes mellitus and heart attacks, the fifth and first killers in the Western world respectively. The ultimate seat of human well-being came thus to be seen as residing in the large bowel, just as my grandmother, who was not an educated woman, but whom experience had taught a thing or two, had always maintained. She believed that what she called a weekly clearout, procured by a spoonful of castor oil, was both a necessary and a sufficient condition for health. Not coincidentally, she lived to a ripe old age.

Interestingly, however, the epidemiological tide seems to be turning against dietary fibre. It seems that you really can have too much of a good thing, after all. Those who sprinkle bran on everything they eat – no doubt with the self-righteous expression often seen upon the faces of the joggers as they pass the evening strollers in the park – are subject to a variety of complaints, the consequence apparently of malnutrition consequent upon malabsorption of vital nutrients. How are the bulky fallen!

The salt cycle will be repeated and then extended, for the arguments so compellingly in favour of interference in the public's consumption of salt will be equally compelling for interference in whatever is discovered next to be a deadly poison. (The timing of the campaign against salt is probably not coincidental, the battle against tobacco having virtually been won, or at least on the ideological, if not the practical, plane. No new facts about salt have come to light, but epidemiologists are the last people on earth to rest on their laurels.)

Not that governments are reluctant, exactly, to be pressured into interfering ever more insistently (and insidiously) in the daily lives of those who fall under their jurisdiction. In Britain – surely not unique in this regard – the government has changed the relationship between doctor and patient from that of adviser, healer and comforter (all at the patient's behest) to that of bureaucratic executor of a governmental plan. The doctors are bribed and threatened into performing large numbers of allegedly preventive tests on their patients which have a minimal chance of benefiting any individual patient – because the government thinks they should. The doctors' opinions are as irrelevant as those of their patients.*

Even if the British government were entirely well advised in its plans – even if it had not plucked targets for doctors to aim for at random from a statistical sky of its own imagining – and even if, *per impossibile*, it were wholly well intentioned and its motives were undilutedly benevolent, even if the implementation of its plan were to produce some increase in longevity or decrease in morbidity, this would still not entail that the plan ought to be implemented. (Of one thing we may be sure, however: if life expectancy rises after the implementation of the plan, the rise will be attributed to its wisdom and that of its devisers.) The fact that people who have no symptoms have repeatedly to attend for check-ups, rather like commercial aircraft of a certain age which may suffer from metal fatigue unbeknown to their pilots, destroys even the conceptual possibility of feeling truly and completely

---

* In the United States, where insurance companies take on the role which in Britain is played by the government, it has been estimated that the average citizen will be enjoined or cajoled into visiting the doctor 274 times between the ages of twenty and seventy, not because he or she is ill – visits caused by illness will be extra, though they will remain a small proportion of the total – but merely for checks of one kind or another, allegedly to prevent future illnesses, but largely, one suspects, to remind the citizenry of the constant need for doctors, insurance companies and perpetual anxiety about health.

well. In a world of preventive medicine, however well one actually feels, there may still be – in fact, there almost certainly is – a time bomb ticking away deep in the bowels of one's body. Does it not, after all, take time, perhaps several years or even decades, for a cancer to manifest itself in symptoms? Is it not likely, then, that somewhere deep inside me, even as I write, malignant cells have already arisen and are dividing and multiplying? Would it not be prudent of me, therefore, now that I have reached the cancerable age, to have myself scanned from head to toe, so that I can arrest the disease before it truly begins? And if I am clear of that disease today, should I not repeat the whole process tomorrow? Bear in mind that carcinogenesis must make itself manifest to such a scan at one point or another, and life is too precious to be lost by unnecessary or feckless delay.

It is clear that screening for diseases, from the vast majority of which we shall never suffer, adds to our already considerable difficulties in losing ourselves, and contributes powerfully to that self-absorption which trivialises all cogitation and art alike, and envenoms existence itself.

It is highly unlikely that the government – the present, or any other – will ever run out of targets for its supposedly well-intentioned interference in our lives. The number of risk factors which have been identified for heart attacks, still the most frequent cause of death in the Western world despite a dramatic but ill-publicised reduction in the last decade or two, exceeds three hundred. Admittedly, some of them – male-pattern baldness, for example, or being first-born – are not readily amenable to governmental intervention; but others, such as low selenium and zinc levels in the blood, most certainly are.

Of the provocation of anxiety there is no end; and so long as health at any price is our goal, governments will never lack a *locus standi* (or *casus belli*) for telling us what to eat, do and even think.

III

But are we really more obsessed with our health than ever before? Medical messiahs have been around for a long time, since the beginning of the eighteenth century at least. The cornflake, the breakfast food which is only slightly more appetising than the packaging in which it comes, was invented at the end of the nineteenth century by a doctor whose bizarre beliefs would scarcely have been out of place today, and could only have become popular in a population which was already inclined to worry about its health and therefore ready to believe that the bland or unappetising must be healthful.

Nevertheless, the emphasis on health matters seems to have become considerably more marked in the last twenty years. Every newspaper now has its health page, and recently on a train I noticed a man reading a newspaper which proudly announced on its front page that it had no fewer than twelve pages inside devoted to health. (The lead article of these twelve pages asked the question 'Can dieting lower your IQ?' – so that henceforth readers might simultaneously worry about excess mortality from being too fat and becoming demented from trying to do something about it.) In one edition alone of the *Daily Telegraph*, I counted more than twenty articles connected with health.

Even provincial newspapers are not immune from this excessive interest in health. *El Heraldo* of Cartagena, Colombia, contained in its edition of 2 December 1996 a column with the following information: that two students at Cardiff University had died of meningitis, one of them falling ill at a lecture in the afternoon and dying in the evening; that British scientists had discovered that a third of fat women might carry and store carcinogens in their adipose tissue, leading to a higher rate of cancer of the breast than average; and that Russian scientists had announced that an asteroid, measuring four kilometres by two, had passed within 5,300,000 kilometres of the earth, which it approached with an unpredictable trajectory every four years and which – if it ever collided with the earth – would cause such damage that the whole of the human race would be wiped out. What is the average reader of *El Heraldo* to make of all this? A reasonably assiduous reader of one such newspaper alone is likely to be subjected to more than one thousand health items per annum.

Women's magazines now have more articles about health than ever before. They have always had a doctor to answer readers' questions, of course; but comparing popular women's magazines of today with those of, say, sixty years ago, it is obvious even on a cursory inspection that the principal change has been in the medicalisation of the contents. No such magazine is nowadays complete without several medical stories, usually of a horrifying, dramatic or inspiring kind, designed to give rise to a witches' brew of emotions such as anxiety, pity and over-optimism; but in other respects – the gossip about well-known figures, the short stories in which women of no particular standing are swept off their feet by a love affair into an exciting, affluent and socially more elevated life – the magazines have scarcely changed.

One is never too young to become a hypochondriac or to start worrying unrealistically about one's health: magazines for teenagers are now also full of health stories. The readers of today are the *worried well* (to use the cant term of the hour) of tomorrow. He or she is the consumer of the panaceas and quack remedies of the future.

If you go into any bookshop in the Western world, you will find that books about health – diets for arthritis, psychological methods of overcoming discomforts, etc. – exceed in number and volume those devoted to the history of the world.

This suggests that the inclusion of health items in the news bulletins on both radio and television, a phenomenon of relatively recent origin, is indeed a response to market, or at least market research, forces. I have been told by acquaintances working in radio and television that it is now a laid-down *requirement* that news bulletins should carry at least one item about health, whether or not there is anything worthy of report, and whatever else may have been happening in the wider world.

These health items are either about the development of a miracle cure for a disease from which only a vanishingly tiny minority of the viewers or listeners can possibly be suffering (miracle cures which generally fail to live up to their initial sensational promise); or about a scandalous shortcoming in, or shortage of, medical services; or about cases of spectacular medical incompetence; or about an unprecedented threat to the health of mankind as a whole (threats which also generally fail to live up to their full potential). The emotional pendulum thus swings with ever-increasing swiftness between grateful wonderment at the advances in medical science and technology on the one hand, and gusts of deep anxiety about distant eventualities on the other.

My first intimation of the anxieties which news stories about health could arouse came to me some years ago while I was holding a morning clinic. A woman telephoned to tell me that she had just eaten a slice of bread and butter and salmon paste. Unbeknown to me – for I have long had an aversion to the broadcast news – there had been a news item on the radio about a woman who had died of botulism (a rare but dramatic form of food poisoning) after eating some tinned salmon.

'Thank you for calling and letting me know,' I said.

'But do you think I'll be all right, doctor?' she asked.

'Well, I don't much care for salmon paste myself,' I replied, 'but I should think so.'

'You don't think I'll get botulism, then?' she asked in all seriousness.

For those with slightly longer memory spans than average, who retain information and even hoard it, but do not realise that the purpose of our media of mass communication is not to inform but to entertain (and there is nothing more entertaining than a good scare), the consequences of this deliberately induced anxiety about health can be severe. I recall a recent patient of mine who was suffering from a mortal condition which would, unfortunately, kill her in one or two years' time, but who refused to eat anything because of the hidden dangers entailed in the consumption of anything and everything. Though she had starved herself nigh unto death, her appetite was unimpaired. Cheese was forbidden her because of the risk

of listeria; fish because of heavy metals; chicken and eggs
because of salmonella; vegetables because of insecticides
and fungicides; red meat because of cholesterol; prepared
foods because of the radiation used in their preservation,
carcinogenic wrappings and E numbers; milk because of
the hormones used in its production; and so forth. The list
of prohibitions was endless. Whatever food was suggested
to her, she had her objection to it at the ready, possessed as
she was of an elephantine memory for health items on the
news and in the newspapers; and so eating, which might
have been one of her few consolations in her last months on
earth, became impossible for her, every mouthful a victory
for her devoted but tormented husband but an occasion of
agonising anxiety for her.

Of course, most people do not remember the exact
contents of the health items on the broadcast news or in the
newspapers for longer than a few days at most. (Given the
average contents of television programmes, I derive some
comfort from the fact that a large percentage of the
patients I have visited at home who have had the television
on when I arrived – that is to say, nearly all of them –
cannot tell me with any degree of coherence what they were
watching *then*, at that moment, let alone the contents of
what they were watching in the immediate or remote past.)
But that is not say that they leave no trace whatsoever: on
the contrary, the overall impression they give to those who
watch and read is that we live in unusually dangerous
times, from the point of view of our health. There are, in
fact, dangers lurking everywhere, even in those things by
which we set most store and which we previously considered safe.

Increasingly, advertising hoardings convey the same
message, some of them the outpourings of quasi-govern-

mental organisations. On emerging from the prison where I work, and outside which someone was recently shot dead in a war between drug gangs (and outside which shortly afterwards another man was found waiting with a gun), I observed in quick succession two hoardings, the first with a large picture of a banana, to convey the message that accidents at work were frequent and serious – though how such a hoarding would help to reduce either the frequency or the seriousness of such accidents was not explained – and the second with the following words in huge lettering on a lurid red background: 'Am I at risk?' Of what, one might ask? Of the thousand natural shocks that flesh is heir to? No: if one looked carefully, one found the words Meningitis and Septicaemia, and a telephone number to ring in case of anxiety. These two posters were examples of what elsewhere I have called the permanent effervescence of publicly funded panic.

I watch little television myself, but to my chagrin a set has been installed in one of the wards in which I work, and it is switched on almost permanently and is inescapable for the six patients as they lie in their beds. (Whatever happened to the idea that hospitals should be havens of peace rather than resorts of entertainment?) Like the patients, I therefore catch glimpses of programmes whether I wish to or not. The percentage of such programmes with a medical content astonishes me: misdiagnoses by incompetent doctors, surgical operations which went horribly wrong, deadly but previously unsuspected side effects of commonly used drugs and so forth. Whether this is suitable viewing and listening for people who are themselves seriously ill I am inclined to doubt; suffice it to say that they are not permitted even to die in the belief that their troubles will then be over once and for all, for I once arrived on

the ward to find an acrimonious discussion being relayed at
high volume about the incompetence, greed and dishonesty
of undertakers.

Perhaps the enormous increase in the attention given to
matters of health is simply a function of the enormous
expansion in the number of channels of mass communication. It is the existence of these channels which creates
the need to communicate something, and not vice versa.
Hypochondriasis is one of the most easily evoked passions
of the soul, and is literally endless in its scope. Health is
therefore the ideal subject for channels of mass communication, which are at a loss to fill the time and space
available to them. In these times of social isolation, when
more people than ever before live alone, in single-person
households with very limited contact with other human
beings, symptoms are often the only real companions they
have, old friends in whose slight variations and ups and
downs they take a profound interest, as people once did
in the gossip concerning their neighbours. A visit to the
doctor is the nearest many people come to a social
engagement.

Hypochondriacs there have always been, of course, and
hypochondriacs there will always be. Argan, the protago-
nist of Molière's play *Le Malade imaginaire*, is instantly
recognisable to us today. And were the reasons given for the
shortness of human life by the eighteenth-century English
physician George Cheyne so very different from those given
by latter-day pedlars of sublunary immortality? According
to Cheyne, God was

> obliged (that the Globe of the Earth might not, from
> the long lives of its inhabitants, become a Hell and a
> Habitation for incarnate Devils) to shorten their lives

from 900 or 1,000 years, to 70. He wisely foresaw that animal Food and artificial Liquors would naturally contribute towards this End; and indulged, or permitted, the Generation that was to start the Earth again after the Flood, the Use of these for Food; knowing that though it would shorten the lives and plait a Scourge of Thorns for the Backs, of the Lazy and Voluptuous, it would be cautiously avoided by those who knew it was their Duty and Happiness to keep their Passions low, and their Appetites in subject.

In other words, eat vegetables, don't drink, keep exercising and perhaps you, too, can live a life of antediluvian longevity. Cheyne's doctrine would not be out of place on any modern chat show, in any self-help book, or on any keep-fit video.*

What is undoubtedly new in modern hypochondriasis, though, is the unique inappropriateness and redundancy of the anxieties suffered by millions of people. They frighten themselves with trifles, the better to avoid contemplation of the void at the heart of their existence.

---

* Cheyne himself was a very interesting figure. His famous book, *The English Malady*, published in 1733, first made fashionable the idea that disgruntlement and vague ill-health were signs of superior sensibility (an idea from whose influence we still have not entirely escaped). He pandered, in effect, to the anxieties of a leisured class of unprecedented size and wealth. He was not altogether successful, however, at following his own advice regarding moderation as the great preserver of health: at one point in his life he weighed 448 pounds. *Le patron n'est pas au régime ici.* A servant walked behind him with a stool so that he could pause for rest every few yards. One is irresistibly reminded of the late Jim Fixx, the high priest of jogging, who spent six years of his waking life at the very least – that is to say, more than a sixth of his adult existence – avoiding the very heart attack which killed him at the age of fifty-two.

IV

Information without perspective is a higher form of ignorance. There are many reasons why it should be so difficult nowadays first to develop and then to maintain a sense of perspective.

First, the pace of technical progress is so rapid that one forgets almost immediately what life was like before the development of the latest gadget whose existence is taken for granted within days of acquisition. Who nowadays recalls that it was once a time-consuming affair (and an event of some importance) to place a telephone call to a town outside a short radius of one's home? I am talking now not of prehistory, but of four decades ago at most, supposedly well within the memory of half the population. I myself have difficulty in remembering what my life was like before I owned my first computer, so essential a daily tool has it become to me, even though more than three-quarters of my existence has been lived without one.

Rapid technical progress, therefore, has the effect of disconnecting us from our own pasts, to say nothing of the past of our society as a whole. But without constant reconnections to our past, life becomes an eternal present moment, and its problems are correspondingly magnified by lack of anything with which to compare them. When my telephone fails to put me in touch instantaneously with, say, Haiti (to take an example from my recent experience), I am inclined to throw it at the wall in frustration, rather than to reflect on the marvels of technical progress which have led to me expect such a communication as a matter of course. In truth, there is nothing quite as stale as yesterday's progress.

Second, rapid technical progress has the effect of turning our attention to future possibilities rather than to past difficulties and constraints. It does, however, bring into sharp relief present limitations, which seem immense by comparison with the Aladdin's cave of the infinite prospects which technology will soon open to us. We are promised wonders, for example, from the development of genetic engineering, and from the elucidation of the human genome: when all is known, there will be no more congenitally defective children, and in so far as the age at which we die is genetically determined we shall be able to prolong our lives with a little tinkering in the chromosomes. Indeed, the ageing process itself will be understood and tamed: and death shall have no dominion.

This is splendid – or at least it will be, for those who live to see it. The trouble is that not all of us *will* live to see it, which is a terrible injustice. All we have done wrong is to be born too early, which was beyond our control; so why should those born after us have everlasting life, and even youth, merely by virtue of having delayed a little their entry into the world? They will have contributed nothing to their own good fortune: they will be the idle immortal.

When the prospect of an illness-free and endless existence beckons (it matters not at all whether this prospect is realistic from the scientific point of view or not, it has only to be believed to beckon), it is not surprising that the thousand natural shocks that flesh is heir to should be experienced as unjust. We are enjoined, when suffering, always to remember those less fortunate than ourselves who are suffering even more, in the hope that this will console us; but the reason why we have so constantly to be enjoined in this fashion is that we more naturally turn our envious gaze towards those who are more, not less, fortunate than we. The possibility – or probability – that those who come after us will enjoy incomparably better conditions of existence than we is not entirely pleasing or consoling. Only those who look backwards with satisfaction can truly enjoy that unjustly much-maligned state of mind, complacency. It is difficult, after all, to conceive of any form of human happiness in which complacency does not play its part.

Third is a loss of sense of history, which might otherwise have lent perspective to our present anxieties over our health. I am not now referring to sheer ignorance of history, though this, at least in a large part of the population of Britain, is of truly astonishing extent.* The least educated are not, on the whole, the worst or most chronic hypochondriacs, though they are certainly the unhealthiest section of the population and may temporarily be laid low

---

* The literal truth. Many, perhaps most, of my patients between the ages of fifteen and twenty have not heard of the Battle of Hastings, and the year 1066 does not ring even the faintest of bells with them; they cannot give the dates of the Second World War, not even to within the nearest fifty years. When asked to name a British prime minister other than the present incumbent or Mrs Thatcher, almost all of them say that they cannot, adding by way of explanation that they weren't born then. After eleven years of compulsory education, or rather attendance at school, it has not yet been imparted to them that it is possible to know things other than by personal acquaintance. Moreover, they see no more reason to know something about the past than about anything else. 'There are no jobs,' they say. This is the end result, the *reductio ad absurdum*, of the view of life in general and the economy in particular as a zero sum game, a view assiduously peddled over the years by many intellectuals who are philosopher-kings *manqués*.

by fears of the spread of Ebola virus, for example, having watched a number of films in which the earth was invaded by monsters, aliens and diseases from outer space, memories of which are reawakened by stories of dread diseases emanating from the Congo. But on the whole, the worst educated lack staying power once anxieties about their health are raised, and soon slump back into indifference, resuming their unhealthy habits. From the point of view of psychiatrists, however, it is just as well that human anxiety is not necessarily proportional to the objective situation, otherwise few people would ever need to consult them.

The lack of a sense of history of which I speak is that from which even the knowledgeable may suffer: that is, if they assent to the school of historiography which sees the whole of the human past as a justification for, and precursor of, modern disgruntlements. It is true that Gibbon once wrote that history is nothing but the record of mankind's crimes and follies; but then Gibbon was an urbane ironist, which cannot, on the whole, be said of today's *enragés*, who are inclined to see in all the achievements of the past only more sophisticated methods of oppressing whichever minority happens to be the cynosure of their compassion. (Oddly enough, they often belong to that very minority themselves. Modern compassion is often rather difficult to distinguish from self-pity.)

Why this particular school of historiography should be so popular nowadays is a question somewhat beyond my present scope. Suffice it to say that, after Auschwitz and the gulag, it has been generally felt that only those who have suffered horribly can have anything worthwhile or profound to say about human affairs, or can speak with full moral authority. Since everyone with a minimum of education naturally believes that he has something worthwhile and profound to say, and speaks with moral authority, it follows that he must have suffered – and still suffers – horribly.*

In this peculiar historiography, the horrors of the past may be admitted, but never to draw the conclusion – so wounding to our *amour propre* – that we are by far the most fortunate people who have ever existed (at least from the material standpoint). The horrors of the past are made to serve a quite different purpose: namely, to inculpate the intellectual and material descendants and beneficiaries of those whom the historiography holds responsible for those very horrors; and to suggest, moreover, that only those who grasp the historiography understand how the continuing horrors may be eliminated from the world.

Not long ago, I read an interesting monograph on Aztec medicine which went into great and scholarly detail about the medicinal plants used by the ancient Mexicans. It was excellent in its way, and very learned, though the author accepted claims for the medicinal efficacy of the plants with rather less scepticism than he might have applied to claims for the products of giant modern pharmaceutical companies.

He contrasted the medical knowledge of the Aztecs with that of the invading Spaniards, and found it superior. So eager was he, in fact, to demonstrate the all-round superiority of the Aztecs over the Spaniards (except in the one crucial regard of killing large numbers of their enemies in

* One of the leaders of the 1960s student revolt in the United States, Mark Rudd, wrote an article entitled 'You don't know what hell is unless you were raised in Scarsdale'. Scarsdale is an upper-middle-class suburb of New York. The article was not intended as a joke – the author apparently meant what he wrote. At the same time, he must have had a still, small voice telling him that there were worse fates that could befall a human being than that of having been born in the lap of luxury.

a short time) that he stated that, at the time of the Conquest, the Aztec population was generally healthy and suffered from few, if any, serious epidemic or other diseases. His evidence for this was that the Aztecs lived longer, on average, than the Spanish of the epoch.

This may well have been the case, but the figure he himself gave for the life expectancy of the Aztecs, 37.5 years, suggests that they were subject to a number of quite serious diseases after all. No population with a life expectancy between a quarter and a third lower than that of Haiti today could possibly be called healthy: infant mortality must have been very high and survival to what we should consider old age rare. Many horrible diseases (to which, of course, the Spanish soon added many others of a far more devastating nature) must have been prevalent. Compared with their Aztec forebears, the most downtrodden indigenes of Mexico today must appear a picture of rude health, to say nothing of the Mexican population as a whole. By emphasising in Rousseau-esque fashion the good health of the Aztecs, the repulsive idea is kept at bay that, despite all the vagaries of history, which include all the atrocities which the human mind can devise, there has been progress, and that this progress is wholly attributable to the Western intellectual tradition of the last five centuries.

I do not, of course, ascribe this dramatic improvement to wise or benevolent government. Technical advance is the motor of such progress, and it spreads with increasing rapidity throughout the entire globe. That is why it is unwise to assess the moral standing of governments by any improvements in the life expectancy of the citizenry under their sway, though declines in life expectancy may well be the result of their unwise or brutal policies. Few people realise, for example, that the health of the population of

Guatemala improved more under thirty years of military dictatorship than that of the population of Cuba under thirty years of communism. It seems to me that this does not settle once and for all the question of the relative moral grandeur of Guatemalan guerrillas and Cuban caudillos. But it is interesting to note how intellectuals have used health care to raise hosannahs to communist dictators, first as if there were no health care anywhere else except under such dictatorships, and second as if the treatment of illness were the most important, or sole, aim of life, which justified gulags, purges, terrors and extravagant cults of personality.

The historiography which uses the past as a backward projection of the present finds it impossible to acknowledge or embrace the fact of progress wholeheartedly; for if it did, it might, among other things, force us to abandon our self-pitying hypochondriasis. It is an historiography which prevents us from entering imaginatively into the life of the past, but, on the contrary, seeks to insert our present-day preoccupations into that life. History is thus the continuation of disgruntlement by other means.

V

There is, of course, another reason for our preoccupation with illness and its worst consequence, death: namely, our unfamiliarity with either. Like the child who knows the name of no prime ministers from the time before he can remember, our direct acquaintance with the dissolution of the flesh is practically nil. As soon as anyone around us is seriously ill, he or she is whisked off to hospital, put into a nice clean bed and connected to a variety of machines which offer the hope of eternal life. And hospitals are such busy, bustling places – so apparently convinced of their own importance – that it is impossible to imagine that much of their activity is, from the point of view of prolonging life, perfectly futile. It would be ungrateful, in fact, to suggest such a thing to any of the staff, who are quite clearly not only dedicated but rushed off their feet, and who might not be able to keep going, might collapse like a pricked balloon, if any hint of resignation in the face of the inevitable were to enter their philosophy.

Our streets, though crowded, are practically free of seriously ill, maimed or deformed people. In the whole history of humanity (at least in its so far brief civilised stage) this is unprecedented. If you go to the poorest cities of the world, you cannot avoid people with withered limbs, who are clearly malnourished, who are racked by chronic fevers, or who are disfigured by hideous ulcerating sores. Around your feet there will sooner or later pass a paraplegic, dragging himself along pitifully, using his arms like oars and the ground like water. You will be reminded that pus smells, that flies adore raw human flesh, that eyes are vulnerable to accident and infection: things which you have never had reason to recall before.

Another indication of our growing unfamiliarity with pathology can be gleaned from a comparison of the textbooks which teach medical students how to examine patients published nowadays and, say, sixty years ago. The photographs in the earlier textbooks show people suffering from such gross pathology that one would be hard-pressed not to notice it; whereas nowadays the signs of illness are far more subtle, and can easily escape untutored observation. It is not merely that we now succeed in keeping the grossly deformed out of sight because of our increased fastidiousness in this regard, but also that such people exist in far smaller numbers. One of the reasons the epidemic of AIDS was so alarming was that, in this age of deodorised death, it behaved like a biblical plague in slow motion. Death is expected to behave itself more discreetly these days, taking people off by subtle processes confined to the inside of the body, invisible to the naked eye and nostril. In so far as the existence of death is acknowledged at all, it is expected to behave itself (as a *quid pro quo*) with a certain decorum. The difference between death's conduct nowadays and its conduct in the past is – or should be – that between the drug cartels of Cali and Medellin: the one diffident, retiring, gentlemanly, and violent only when necessary; the other brash, vulgar, and violent by preference.

However unfamiliar by personal acquaintance we may be with serious illness, we are a hundred times less familiar with death. Many of us have at least visited a seriously ill person in hospital, however much the hospital atmosphere may have diluted the experience; but it is doubtful whether more than a small percentage of us have ever so much as caught a glimpse of a dead body, let alone touched one. Not long ago, a man aged sixty-two came to me in an extreme state of panic because he had found someone dead – a person, incidentally, with whom he had no emotional connection. He must have sensed my no doubt disdainful surprise that he should have been so affected by it, for he said, 'You see, doctor, I've never seen a dead body before.'

This must surely be the first epoch in recorded history in

which a man could reach the age of sixty-two without ever having seen the corpse of one of his fellow men. Indeed, the mere sight of a body is sufficient nowadays to provoke that aggregation of nervous symptoms the Post-Traumatic Stress Disorder.

In Africa, by contrast, death is visible even on the streets. Several times I have seen naked bodies in the gutters of the roads in Nigerian cities, for example, with cars and pedestrians streaming by with apparent unconcern. Whatever else may be true of Nigerians, it is unlikely that many of them ever long forget that human life hangs by a thread and always ends in death.

My own father's death was averagely sanitised, no doubt to spare my feelings. I was informed by telephone that, as expected, he had died in his sleep overnight (perhaps helped by liberal doses of opiate drugs) and that I should come to the hospital to collect his things. Once there, I was handed not only a plastic bag containing those belongings, but a booklet – very useful in its own way – explaining the bureaucratic formalities after someone has died. There were the death certificates to be collected, tax authorities to be informed, neighbours to be notified, gas and electricity meter readings to be taken, and so forth. Death was thus transformed from an existential into a bureaucratically complex moment, an irritating interruption to the normal flow of life rather than the occasion of reflection about life's meaning and how it should be lived. The inconvenience was of the same order of magnitude as that caused by a burglary.

As for the disposal of the dead, we entrust it to the experts, the undertakers, of whose activities we have only the faintest notion. They do whatever it is they do behind closed doors; and even their most public activities take

place behind heavily frosted windows. Their fundamental
duty, one suspects, is to protect us from contact with the
dead, for fear that such contact might destroy our illusions
about our own immortality.

Gone are the funeral processions of the past, with their
black plumes, their solemnity and ceremoniousness. No
one wears mourning nowadays, though black may be a
fashionable colour in some years. We go to funerals these
days as a respectable man enters a pornographer's shop or
picks up a prostitute, with shame in our hearts and embarrassment on our faces. We want it all over as quickly as
possible, so that we may resume the activities which will
continue to occupy us for ever. The dead disappear from
our thoughts as pebbles disappear from view when
dropped in a pond.

In African villages, there are funeral processions almost
every week, the entire population trailing behind the pall-
bearers, who trudge towards the village burial place with
crude, home-made coffins (often tiny, to contain a child)
on their shoulders. No lugubrious professional, paid to look
glum, comes between the body of the deceased and his
relatives, so that by the age of five almost everyone has
seen, and perhaps touched, the dead.

But where is death – or its precursor, mortal sickness –
to be seen among us? Our streets are full of immortals,
taller, healthier, better-fed people than have ever existed
before. If death should strike, it must be but rarely, and
then only by accident.

Our unfamiliarity with death is a consequence, no
doubt, of the good health which we have come to accept
(and expect) as normal. But the unfamiliar is frightening,
as is the unlikely; and men fear death as children fear to go
in the dark, whether it cuts a swathe through the popula-

tion in epidemics or picks us off stealthily one by one, so that we hardly notice its advance upon us.

VI

Just how unfamiliar with death we are by comparison with our ancestors – not such remote ones either – can be grasped by a little historical demography.

When Man first began to cultivate the earth and inhabit fixed settlements, his life expectancy declined. This is not to say, however, that there was a prelapsarian golden age in which Man, the happy hunter-gatherer, lived in perfect harmony with a generous environment, into which he melted like butter in hot potatoes. Alas, hunter-gatherers rarely lived to be forty, and the slightest graze must easily have proved fatal to them. The noble savage did not gain his nobility through his long experience of life.

When Man first began to congregate in any numbers, in cities, the state of his health deteriorated further. The new density of population allowed the spread of epidemic diseases which until then were unknown. The life expectancy in ancient Egypt and Rome was about 25, at which it remained – give or take a few years – until the beginning of the eighteenth century. Then it began to rise, and has risen uninterruptedly since, through the horrors of the Industrial Revolution, through wars as devastating as the Napoleonic and First and Second World Wars, and

through the Great Depression of the 1930s.* The life
expectancy in the average advanced industrialised country
is now three times longer than that of ancient Rome or
Hanoverian London.

What did a life expectancy of 25 mean, the life
expectancy which prevailed throughout most of recorded
history? It meant an infant mortality rate of at least 250:
that is to say, of 1,000 babies born alive, at least 250 would
have been dead within a year of their birth. About half
would have been dead by the age of five. The survivors
would have been comparatively long-lived, with an average life expectancy of 45: in other words, they would have
survived to what we should nowadays call early middle
age. Those who survived to genuine old age were few,
which is perhaps one of the reasons why most societies
before our own accorded such respect to the old. Survival
then appeared a remarkable achievement, attributed no
doubt to some special moral quality in the survivor.

Of course, there was a social gradient in life expectancy
– there always is. In the nineteenth century, for example,
there were boroughs in the industrial parts of England in
which the average age at death was less than 18. These
boroughs acted as a magnet to the poorest of the poor, and
it is doubtful whether more terrible conditions have existed
anywhere, at least in peacetime. And it is worth recalling
that the life expectancy of members of the British Royal
Family, which then as now was not without economic

---

* One of the few instances of a prolonged and serious reversal of this
trend has occurred in Russia during the last two decades, where the life
expectancy of men has actually fallen, thus proving that Dostoevsky and
the Slavophiles were right all along: that Russia is not as other countries
are, but has a special destiny of its own. And thus the intemperate use
of spirits has achieved what Lenin and Stalin, for all their savagery,
could not do, at least in the long term.

resources, was about 44 years in the middle of the nineteenth century.

The political purposes to which this gradient in life expectancy is put are not without interest. For a long time now the *British Medical Journal* in particular has been using the relative deterioration of the health of the lowest social class in Britain *vis-à-vis* the health of the highest social class as a stalking horse for demanding more government expenditure on social and health services for the (relatively) poor. One sometimes senses that it regards taxation of the rich as good in itself, irrespective of the social or economic effects produced, and it would pass sumptuary laws if it could. There is an unspoken element of masochism in all this because, of course, doctors are still among the richest section of the population who would be taxed more heavily under the new dispensation. On the other hand, they would perhaps be able to console themselves for the higher taxes they paid with the higher salaries they would receive from the proceeds – not for nothing is the wage bill of the Health Service about 80 per cent of its total cost.

The *BMJ*'s agitation on behalf of the poor is based upon the following considerations. Over a number of years the health indicators of the poorest section of the population have deteriorated relative to those of the richest. Let us take the infant mortality rate as an example: it is generally accepted by epidemiologists (though not by me) as being the most sensitive index available of the social welfare of a population. Twenty years ago, the ratio of the infant mortality rates of the poorest to the richest section of the population was 1.6:1. It is now 2.0:1 (that is to say, twice as many infants born to the lowest social class die in their first year of life as infants born to the highest social class).

Ergo, the condition of the poor has deteriorated, and the increased inequality of outcome represents a state of worsening social injustice, which needs to be redressed by increased governmental intervention and expenditure.

This is not the place to discuss at length the concept of social justice as equality of outcome. Personally, I do not think they are in the least compatible: justice surely requires regard to the conduct of individuals, even the poor, who are no less conscious of what they do than the rich, though their choices may be considerably more limited in practice. Nothing could be less just, after all, than equality of outcome for widely different courses of action. But the *BMJ* evidently considers that equality of outcome *is* synonymous with social justice, for otherwise it would not automatically regard increased differentials, whether of income or infant mortality rate, as evidence of increased social injustice. It adheres to a version of Hamlet's rather perfunctory theory of justice: treat each man after his desert, and who should 'scape whipping? Instead of whipping, of course, it would distribute equal sums of money and other goods to everyone, but the principle is the same as Hamlet's. It is quite beyond the powers of the *BMJ* to imagine a situation in which increased differentials would represent more, not less, justice – because it cannot distinguish between kindness, decency, mercy and justice, an inability which is the result of supposing that all human desiderata must be compatible with one another and are achievable by a single unblemished policy. Thus it is perfectly conceivable that kindness and decency would require inequalities to be reduced, but not justice, which would require that they be maintained. Unfortunately, in this world of perpetually inflamed and resentful egos, which thirst for victimhood as the Christians of old thirsted for martyrdom, justice has assumed the role of Queen of the Virtues, as theology was once the Queen of the Sciences, and once a question has been made one of justice no other considerations are allowed to enter into the discussion of it. At the mere mention of the word, we all turn into monomaniacs.

What the *BMJ* so singularly omits to mention (apart from changes in the composition of the population, such that the higher social classes enlarge in size while the lower contract) in its frequent discussions of the topic – which are not dissimilar from those in many other organs of opinion – is that relative risk is much less important for the fate of the individual than absolute risk, especially when the risk is small in the first place. Would we prefer our relative risk to fall while our absolute risk rises, or vice versa? If equality were important in itself to us, we should prefer the former to the latter, but this is clearly absurd. Would an infant mortality rate of, say, 200 per thousand, which affected all social classes equally, be preferable to an infant mortality rate of 12 in the lowest and 6 in the highest social class (such as we have today), merely because the former satisifed the requirement of justice as equality of outcome while the latter did not? Were conditions better in late-nineteenth-century London because the infant mortality in the best boroughs was 90 per thousand, while that in the worst was 'only' 150; that is to say, only 1.67 times as much? If equality were important in itself as a goal, it would be as well served by raising the infant mortality rate among the rich as by decreasing it among the poor, and would be much easier to achieve into the bargain; but not even the *BMJ* in its most Jacobin mood has yet suggested this solution.

If, on the other hand, the infant mortality rate of the

lowest social class were to be reduced to that of the highest social class, would not the latter be able to argue with equal justice that its relative position had declined, and therefore its situation had deteriorated? We see here in microcosm the way in which improvement can always be presented as deterioration, a most convenient statistical device for those who depend upon public money to fund their work.

It is never explained why the reference point for comparison should be ten or twenty years ago, and not two, thirty, or three hundred years. Nor is it explained why the ratio of infant mortalities across the social classes is the only important statistic to be considered. Why is it unimportant that the absolute infant mortality rate has declined more for the poorest class than for the richest class? But no one in his right mind, surely, would suggest that this constitutes an injustice done to the upper classes.

Some differentials in infant mortality are more important for the *BMJ* than others. All inequalities are unequal, but some are more unequal than others. For example, the infant mortality rate of those born out of wedlock is twice that of those born within wedlock, and this is true even when social class is controlled (i.e. the bastard son of an earl is twice as likely to die in his first year of life as the legitimate son of an earl, though both are unlikely to die). On this differential the *BMJ* has remained notably silent, presumably because the policies which the statistic might suggest to the average person, if implemented, might eventually result in less, rather than more, government expenditure. But this would not be politically correct.

The conclusion seems to me inescapable: that it is the policy recommendations of the *BMJ* – more taxation, more expenditure on health care and social services – which determine the data it presents, rather than the data it presents which determine its policy recommendations. The data it presents are not wrong or inaccurate in themselves; but they are presented in such a way as to create the impression that some kind of crisis exists which would justify drastic measures affecting millions of people. Incidentally, the *BMJ* never recognises that the lowering of the infant mortality rate is not the *sole* aim of government.

In fact, there was a slow improvement in the general health of the population during the nineteenth century, but one indicator remained stubbornly resistant to amelioration: the infant mortality rate. This remained higher in Britain until the first decade of the twentieth century than in some of the poorest countries of Sub-Saharan Africa today: for example, the rate in the London borough in which my father was born, in the year in which he was born, was 124 per thousand, as bad as the rate in modern Zaire, which sends shivers of not altogether unpleasurable horror and indignation down the spines of public health doctors and experts on the Third World. It must be remembered also that at the time of my father's birth, Britain was still an advanced country as far as public health was concerned, compared with countries such as France and Germany; only in New Zealand were conditions appreciably better. Similarly, life expectancy in Britain at the time of my father's birth was a shade lower than that in Haiti today.

Since then, the improvement in the health of the population has been both dramatic and continuous. At the time of the Boer War, the British army was obliged to reject half of the volunteers for service because they failed to meet its not very stringent health requirements. The volunteers struck the medical examiners as pale, stunted, weak fellows, and there was much breast–beating about the degeneration of the race. In fact, these pale, stunted and weak volunteers represented an improvement over their immediate (and distant) ancestors.

There are so many indicators of the vast improvement in the health of the population that one is spoilt for choice. Maternal mortality – the rate of death of mothers during and just after giving birth, as a consequence of doing so – is a good example. A woman in late Elizabethan England had a one in eight or ten chance of dying as a consequence of childbirth. Since on average women gave birth eight to ten times in their lives, one in hundred births resulted in the death of the mother. If the same figure obtained today, there would be 7,800 maternal deaths per year in Great Britain. In 1992, there were 55: that is to say, the rate of death during childbirth was approximately 140 times higher in the late sixteenth century. Since the number of children borne by each woman has declined by at least three-quarters, a woman now suffers a lifetime risk of dying in childbirth less than one five-hundredth of that faced by her Elizabethan forebears. The risk has, in fact, become vanishingly small.

Not all the improvement occurred in the distant historical past. Well within the memory of people who were alive during my lifetime, and at the time of my father's birth, the maternal mortality was sixty-seven times what it is now. In 1900–1902, it was 4.71 per thousand live births; in 1990–92 it was 0.07 per thousand live births. Even between the years 1950–52 and 1990–92, the rate fell by more than nine-tenths.

In 1845, the mortality rate of women giving birth in Vienna's General Hospital was between 10 and 30 per cent; that is to say, between 1,429 times and 4,287 times higher than the rate in modern Britain. They died of puerperal sepsis, and the Hungarian Ignaz Philipp Semmelweis believed that this appalling death rate was the result of infective material brought into the labour ward on the hands of students and doctors, who had performed post-mortems immediately before. By the simple expedient of making them wash and disinfect their hands, he reduced the death rate to 'only' 1 per cent: that is to say, a mere 143 times higher than that of Britain today.*

In 1851, the death rate from respiratory tuberculosis in Britain was more than 440 times that of today. Indeed, the death rate from tuberculosis alone was then more than a quarter of the death rate from *all* causes today, among a population which was very much younger than that which is alive now, and though it was called the Captain of the Men of Death it was far from the only infectious disease to cut a swathe through the population. Other infectious diseases in Victorian Britain caused nearly as many deaths. Typhoid – to take an example of a disease which has since disappeared from our shores – was rampant, and in the year in which it killed Prince Albert it also carried off members of both the Spanish and Prussian royal families. If cancer, stroke and heart attack were comparatively rare in those days, it was only because people did not live long enough to suffer from them.

Perhaps the most dramatic change of all, statistically speaking, has been the decline in the infant mortality rate. As late as 1891, there were streets in Liverpool in which half the children born alive died before their first birthday. In the middle of the nineteenth century wet nurses would let their own children die so that they could continue to

---

* Semmelweis was not believed, and went mad, though whether his insanity was directly caused by the incredulity of his colleagues is a matter for historians and psychiatrists to determine.

suckle the infants of the rich. In 1902, the infant mortality rate in Britain as a whole was 142 per thousand live births; ninety years later, it was 7 per thousand. When I was born, the infant mortality rate was approximately that of most of South America today. What was once a brutal fact of life – the death of an infant – has been transformed by scarcity into a tragedy.

Even within my own comparatively short medical career, there have been striking improvements in the health of the population. For example, in England between the years 1973 and 1991 the death rate from heart attacks under the age of 65 has declined from 85 per 100,000 to 59 per 100,000; while the death rate from strokes for those under the age of 65 declined between the years 1970 and 1990 from 26 per 100,000 to 13. The alarmist advertising hoarding outside the prison where I work notwithstanding, the death rate from accidents has also declined precipitously between 1970 and 1990: from 125 to 59 per 100,000 for those aged over 65, for example, and from 18 to 7 per 100,000 for those aged under 15. And there is no reason to suppose that there will not be further declines.

When I first entered hospital wards as a student (about a quarter of a century ago), their most immediately obvious feature to me as a virtual layman was the number of men and women who suffered from chronic and incurable lung disease – chronic bronchitis and emphysema. Slow death by inability to breathe sufficiently, leading to utter exhaustion both physical and moral, was agonising to behold, let alone to suffer, and one longed for that moment when death was inevitable very soon and it was therefore (implicitly) permissible to administer that dose of morphine which would ease the passing – to use the term of the late Dr Bodkin Adams, who achieved a moment of fame by easing the passing of elderly rich ladies in Eastbourne who had remembered him in their wills.

The generations of blue bloaters and pink puffers, as they were nicknamed by their doctors, have now practically died out, and new cases are, thank goodness, not coming forward in anything like the numbers of old. (Between the years 1984 and 1991 alone, the numbers of deaths from bronchitis and emphysema declined from 1,009 to 378.) This is not to say that our hospital wards now give no unpleasant impression to the lay visitor; on the contrary, they are full of very old people suffering from a number of unpleasant and tragic incurable complaints. But if a steep decline in the numbers of people dying at a comparatively early age from slow suffocation is progress, then there has indeed been great progress.

The decline in the numbers of patients suffering from bronchitis and emphysema is largely attributable to the decline in gross atmospheric pollution and in the consumption of cigarettes. In 1952, a great smog in London was estimated to have caused an excess of 4,000 winter deaths. The Clean Air Act was a necessary and justified response because i) nobody could be expected to clean up his own air, except of course by not smoking; ii) the causal connection between the agent and the illness was undoubted and not in dispute; iii) it was inconceivable that cleaner air would do harm to anyone; iv) the benefit was likely to be great, indeed almost universal; v) acceptable administrative means were at hand to produce the desired result. Compare this to modern attempts by enthusiasts – so far abortive but perhaps not for long – to influence the diet of the entire population. First the connection between the proposed agent – either causative or preventive – and various illnesses is uncertain and a matter of continuing scientific dispute; second, the possibility of harm cannot be discounted in advance of experience, which has not so far been accumulated; third, the numbers of beneficiaries may be very small, at enormous cost to others; fourth, the means to produce the desired effect may well be unacceptably coercive; and fifth, the realm is one in which genuine individual choice exists.

There was one slight loss, however, when the pea-soupers of London became meteorological events of the past: as a child, I thought these fogs were splendid and exciting, and I recall the pleasure I derived from not being able to see the hand in front of my face. Men walked in front of buses to guide them through the gloom; everybody and everything was reduced to an indistinct blur which loomed up out of the swirling greyness at the last moment. For some reason I expected dinosaurs, which I knew to be extant somewhere on earth, to emerge and declare themselves in the November days in London.

When I qualified as a doctor, geriatricians were responsible for patients over the age of sixty-five. A few years later, they were responsible for patients over the age of seventy-five (and not all of them). This was not merely a question of numbers, or of a desire to destroy geriatrics as a medical speciality: a man or woman aged sixty-five was no longer considered old.

Indeed, so long-lived has the population become that economists have started to wonder whether doctors, in saving the lives of middle-aged but still-employed citizens, are adding or subtracting from the wealth of the country in the long term. Nor is it certain that if the population stopped smoking *en masse* any economic benefit would accrue. Not only would the tax revenue be lost, but smokers, who tend disproportionately to die shortly before or after retirement age, would increasingly survive to an unproductive old age. At the moment, many smokers make payments into pension funds for several decades without ever drawing (or drawing for long) a pension, which is obviously of great advantage to non-smokers. Their increased use of medical services during their lifetime is more than offset by the medical savings consequent upon their early deaths. (Indeed, some pension funds are now offering smokers higher pensions to offset their reduced life expectancy.) Perhaps, then, smokers are the unacknowledged philanthropists of the age.

Be that as it may, the fact that the survival of so large a proportion of the population into old age – well past the biblical span – has become something of a problem, at least in the minds of economists, is a powerful testimony to progress, at least if longevity is deemed desirable. For this is the first population in the history of the world in which the great majority can expect to survive into their eighth, ninth or even tenth decade of life.

VII

What brought about this immense and unprecedented demographic change? The precise reasons are far from certain and a matter of historical dispute, but it is generally agreed that the practice of medicine, at least with regard to the treatment of individuals suffering from

serious diseases, could have played but little part, at least
to begin with. For Victorian medicine had little in its arma-
mentarium to distinguish it in point of efficacy from the
most abject quackery.

This fact has led some sociologically minded htstorians
to suppose that the Victorian professionalisation of medical
practice was nothing but a grab for power, money and
gentlemanly status by doctors. After all, if doctors could
offer nothing better than itinerant mountebanks, why
should they have claimed any special powers or privileges?
But this is a very superficial, indeed philistine, point of
view. Even a cursory glance at the pages of *The Lancet* or
the *British Medical Journal* – to say nothing of their
French, German, American and Italian equivalents – would
be sufficient to persuade anyone of the immense, if sometimes fruitless or wasted, intellectual effort which went into
the practice of medicine. Much of this effort was based
upon faith: faith that the human mind was capable of
understanding the way the world worked, and that this
understanding would sooner or later lead to an amelioration of Man's lot in the sublunary world. Vesalius published
his great work of anatomy in 1543 – rightly taken as a
landmark in the history of medicine – but it is doubtful
whether anyone benefited from it in a direct, practical way
for some hundreds of years, until after the discovery of
anaesthesia and asepsis. By contrast, quackery displayed,
and displays, no such endeavour or development: it comes
into the world complete and fully formed, as it were, and
was, and is, the exploitation of gullibility and the placebo
effect for quick profit alone. Recently, for example, on a
bus from Barranquilla to Mompox in Colombia, I witnessed
the performance of a travelling salesman who peddled an
ointment made from 'medicinal herbs'. His ointment was

called *Uña de Gato*, Cat's Claw, and it was good for everything from pain in the kidneys to helping fractious babies
to sleep – simply rub it round their navels. At 30 pence the
tin, he said, he wasn't selling it, he was giving it away.
Gracias por su atención, amigos, y que Dios les bendiga –
thank you for your attention, friends, and may God bless
you. About half the people on the bus bought the pungent
red ointment – the smell and colour of tile polish – and the
salesman moved on to a bus travelling in the opposite
direction. It was a performance unchanged in essence since
the days of Hogarth, if not before. But unlike modern
consumers of quack remedies in richer countries, the
people on the Colombian bus had at least the excuse of a)
a low level of education and b) lack of easy access to
modern medical services.

Not all quackery is equal, however. For example, the
continued popularity of homoeopathy puzzles – and irritates
– many doctors. Actually, it is not so very difficult to
explain. In the nineteenth century, Hahnemann's intellectually ridiculous system had an inherent advantage over the
allopathic medicine of the time, in that his remedies at least
obeyed the great Hippocratic injunction to doctors, first to
do no harm. When one considers the drugs and other means
available to, and used by, the allopathic doctors of the time,
which were all side-effect and no cure, it is hardly surprising that homoeopathy won over adherents.

Oddly enough, this is an advantage which homoeopathy
retains. Bearing in mind that up to 90 per cent of people who
visit their doctors (at least in England) have either a self-
limiting illness or no illness at all, it is clearly an advantage to
be able to prescribe something with no effects at all, side or
otherwise, to which subsequent improvement may be
ascribed. Allopathic doctors, on the other hand, are allowed to

prescribe only drugs with powerful effects, many of which are undesired or undesirable. The advantages of homoeopathy would be destroyed at a stroke if doctors were to resume prescribing pink pills for pale people – though of course they would also need a colourless alternative, since so many people are now allergic to pinkness and other colorations.

The fact remains that, apart from a few palliatives, an equally small number of operations, and vaccination against smallpox (which, though rightly feared, was never responsible for more than a small percentage of overall mortality), Victorian medicine had little which we should nowadays recognise as effective, and that little was insufficient to account for the improvement in the health of the population which began to take place in the nineteenth century. The death rate from tuberculosis started to fall a full century before there was any effective treatment for it, and more than thirty years before its causative organism was discovered. So it was for most of the other great infectious diseases, though the improvements in the water supply – which took place before the germ theory of disease was accepted – led to a sharp decline in the death rate from enteric fevers. Edwin Chadwick, the great British sanitary reformer, was not a doctor (neither was Pasteur); and there have recently been attempts by those historians who cannot accept the fact of progress with a good grace to portray Chadwick and other such reformers as having been motivated more by the need to keep up the supply of labour to expanding British industry, and to avert the threat of revolution from below, than by humanitarian concerns. In such an historiography only out-and-out revolutionaries are truly humanitarian.

It has been calculated – or at least asserted – that it was not until the 1930s that the average patient stood a better chance of receiving benefit than harm from a visit to his doctor. No doubt such a calculation cannot be made with any precision, but it is certain that a modern doctor who reads a medical textbook of no more than sixty years ago will find many of the prescriptions quaint, to say the least. There are doctors still alive who remember that the treatment for lobar pneumonia – then much more common than now – was to inhale oxygen bubbled through brandy. As late as the 1940s, cigarette smoke was recommended by a major British textbook of medicine for the relief of asthma when all else had failed. And it is only since the end of the Second World War that the appreciation that anecdotal evidence is insufficient to establish the curative value of a treatment has become general. The widespread use of controlled trials – in which groups of patients with the same disease are matched as far as possible for other relevant variables, and receive the treatment under investigation or a treatment of previously established efficacy or a placebo, with neither the doctors nor the patients let into the secret of who is receiving what until the end of the trial, so that the possibility of unconscious bias is eliminated – is comparatively recent. Until the 1940s, *ex cathedra* statement to the effect that such and such a treatment is often useful in such and such a condition, based upon no authority other than that of the person making it, were still common in medical textbooks. Much of medical practice was then a rather superior form of superstition, though medical science was laying the foundations for its future therapeutic explosion. Oddly enough, trust in the medical profession seems to be inversely proportional to the scientific basis of its practice: it was accorded most authority when it least deserved it. Such is the way of the world.

Of course, not all medical advances require controlled

trials to establish their value. Some are so dramatic that
such trials are unnecessary: the efficacy of the newly
isolated insulin in the treatment of diabetes, for example.
(Subsequent refinements have required many such trials,
however.) In general, the larger and the more elaborate the
trial necessary to demonstrate the benefit of a treatment,
the smaller that benefit is likely to be: which explains in
part how such vast sums can be spent on medical research
without much advance, except in the researchers' careers.

The inefficacy of most of medical practice until the latter
two-thirds of the twentieth century notwithstanding, the
population continued to enjoy better and better health.
Levels of consumption were rising, and it seems that
consumption is good for you, despite the lucubrations of
the health puritans. With one or two notable exceptions,
wealth is good for health.*

Whether life expectancy would have risen so fast had the
practice of medicine not advanced so dramatically in the
last half-century cannot be answered with certainty, but
there are reasons to suppose that it would have done so in
any case. The influence of health services on the health of
the population, both in the way they are organised and
their degree of technological sophistication, is generally

* One of these minor exceptions is the population – about 4,000 strong
– of the Central Pacific island of Nauru, ten miles in circumference,
where I once did a little work. When it gained its independence from
Australia in 1968, its people suddenly became very wealthy, thanks to
the valuable phosphate rock of which the island's surface was composed.
No longer needing to earn their subsistence, but able to import all they
could eat and drink, they came to consume on average 7,000 calories
per day. Partly as a result of this excessive consumption, and partly no
doubt from a genetic predisposition which had not previously mani-
fested itself, half the population became diabetic and the average life
expectancy was only 47 – lower than that of neighbouring, poorer
islands. The Cuban exception, which is opposite to that of Nauru – that
is to say, health without wealth – is discussed below.

overestimated, at least in Western societies: an overestimation which is both a cause and a symptom of the epidemic – or rather, endemic – hypochondriasis and anxiety about health which grips those societies. Here are the life expectancies (LE) and infant mortality rates (IMR) of several countries:

COUNTRY	LE	IMR
Canada	77	7
Denmark	75	8
France	77	7
Germany	76	8
Greece	77	9
Italy	76	9
Japan	79	5
New Zealand	76	9
Spain	75	9
Sweden	78	6
Switzerland	77	8
United Kingdom	76	8
United States	76	8

The first thing which strikes you on looking at this table is the similarity of the figures for all the countries in it. (Japan is an interesting case: by the end of the last war, health conditions there were nothing short of catastrophic, with life expectancies of 25 for men and 37 for women. Within four decades, the Japanese were the longest-lived people in the world.)

The second striking aspect of this table is the lack of correlation between the sum of money spent by a nation per capita on its health and these crude, but robust, measures of health. Nor is there a correlation between these measures and the way its health services are run, or the technological brio of its doctors. This does not prove, of course, that medical services are unimportant in determining the health of a population; after all, however these services are organised, they are likely to carry out the same emergency procedures for the same life-threatening conditions, besides which it is possible that good medical services could cancel out the effect of relatively bad living conditions, and vice versa. Nevertheless, the singular uniformity of the figures does suggest that longevity is determined by something more fundamental than the minor variations of diet so beloved of epidemiologists, or by the method by which doctors are paid for their services. The fact that Greece has a life expectancy as great – if not greater than – that of the United States seems to me unlikely to be the consequence of the comparative excellence of its doctors. On the contrary, what the figures suggest is that, if a man has enough food to eat, has tolerable shelter, a bacteriologically uncontaminated water supply, and artificially induced immunity against certain diseases, he is likely to live quite a long time.

In short, a long life has become perfectly normal.

VIII

While medicine has probably not played an important part in the increased life expectancy of advanced industrial

nations, it may well have done so in the case of more backward ones. The principal beneficiaries of Western medical
science and technology, therefore, may well have been the
poorer people of the world. It is difficult to disentangle the
effects of medicine from other factors, of course, and few
are the countries which have remained isolated from wider
economic changes and yet have applied modern techno-
logies to public health problems. Certainly, it is possible to
reduce the infant mortality rate (and hence increase the life
expectancy) in poor countries by means of a few techni-
cally – though not administratively – simple means. This is
because the overwhelming majority of infant deaths are
caused by respiratory infections or by gastroenteritis,
which may either be avoided or be treated by uncompli-
cated measures. Even countries as poor as India now have
life expectancies not far short of those of the England into
which I was born, and certainly much in excess of the
England into which my father was born.

Here are the life expectancies and infant mortality rates
of certain Latin American countries:

COUNTRY	LE Male	LE Female	IMR
Argentina	68	72	34
Chile	70	76	14
Colombia	69	72	37
Ecuador	67	73	39
Paraguay	65	69	38
Uruguay	71	78	19
Venezuela	70	76	28

These figures are very similar, one to another; moreover,
they are quite clearly beginning to approximate to those of

the richer countries. The gap between rich and poor (in this respect) is closing, not widening, as is often asserted. Only Africa has been left behind, but even there some improvement has taken place. What has happened in Latin America has also happened in Asia, even more dramatically so.

There is little relationship between the number of doctors and hospital beds, on the one hand, and life expectancy and infant mortality rate on the other. Argentina and Colombia, which have very similar life expectancies and infant mortality rates, have one physician per 376 and 1,078 inhabitants respectively, and one hospital bed per 225 and 693 inhabitants respectively. There is nothing in the climate of Argentina which might explain this apparent paradox.

The gross national products of the above Latin American countries vary by a factor of 7, from approximately one-third to one-twentieth of that of the United States or Germany. The GNP is not a useful or reliable measure of consumption of those goods which are likely to affect health, of course, and in all the above countries the average food intake exceeds the minimum recommended by nutritionists. Moreover, successful efforts have been made to immunise the children of these countries against several common and dangerous diseases of childhood, and to persuade the population that not all water is equally potable, if not actually to provide a supply of such water. Nevertheless, it is clear from the figures above that, within quite wide environmental, social, dietary and economic limits, Man is a tough, resistant and long-lived organism. In short, he does not have to worry himself unduly about his health.

It is in this context that the comparative health of Cuba

should be seen and judged. The immense concentration on health care in Cuba has no doubt resulted in some benefits apart from propagandistic ones, but it is worth recalling that even under the Batista regime Cuba was relatively healthy, with the second best indicators of health in all Latin America.

Curiously enough, Cuba was the scene of one of the few undoubted triumphs of medical science prior to the antibiotic era. I refer, of course, to the eradication of yellow fever from the island while it was under American administration. This eradication required knowledge that yellow fever was spread by the bites of mosquitoes of the *Aedes* genus, knowledge of the habits of these mosquitoes, and the administrative organisation and determination drastically to reduce their numbers. It is fair to say that this episode is not recalled with any fervour on the island today. On the contrary, Cuban historiography prefers to dwell on the alleged primacy of a Cuban doctor of Scottish origin, Carlos M. Finlay, in the scientific discovery of the mosquito transmission of yellow fever. It appears that the American pretender to that honour, Walter Reed, knew of Finlay's prior work, but failed to acknowledge it – the moral of the story being, of course, that you couldn't expect anything else from an American, then or now. Unusually for a medical scientist of the last century, all Finlay's works are still in print in Cuba.

There was a very similar situation in the Rumania of Ceauşescu with regard to the discovery of insulin. The professor of physiology at Bucharest University, Ion Paulescu, was said to have isolated insulin before Banting and Best in Toronto, who, because of their perfidy (typical of people in the capitalist West), failed to recognise the contribution of Paulescu, who has subsequently never received his due. Paulescu's papers, published in a French scientific journal, were still in print in Rumania and were widely distributed, for obvious reasons; but his complete works were not, since – besides being a talented scientist – he was a prominent right-wing nationalist of pronounced anti-Semitic and fascistic stamp.

In fact, controversies over scientific priority are not at all uncommon: Newton went to great lengths to discredit the claims of his rival, Leibniz, to be the inventor of the calculus. Sir Ronald Ross, the discoverer of the mosquito transmission of malaria, engaged in a ferocious and bitter dispute of Byzantine complexity with the Italian researcher Giovanni Battista Grassi over his rival claim to priority. Gallo and Montaignier settled their dispute over priority in the discovery of the virus which causes AIDS not according to the dictates of Truth, but according to the dictates of political expediency, more like Middle Eastern traders haggling over prices in the souk than disinterested seekers after useful knowledge. In these disputes, personal and national pride are often intermingled, and the addition of political ideology to the brew, as in Cuba and Rumania, does little to clarify them.

Much is sometimes made of the fact that the infant mortality rate in Cuba is lower than that of the lower classes and certain ethnic minorities in the United States. But the importance of this is very limited indeed, especially for those who have to make an existential choice about where to live when conditions are intolerable in their native countries. On the whole, they do not flee in the direction of the lowest infant mortality rate. Despite allegations frequently made that health conditions for poor blacks in the United States approximate to those in Third World countries, Haitian refugees (who will join the poor blacks in the United States) show no inclination to risk the short journey from Hispaniola to Cuba for the sake of its excellent free medical care. Even had the reception awaiting them in Cuba been warm rather than hot, it is unlikely that the prospect of open-heart surgery gratis and other medical marvels would have induced them to change their destination of refuge.

Thus the poorest and least educated Haitian peasant may be said to understand something which has escaped the attention of millions of educated, health-conscious middle-class people in North America, Western Europe and Japan: namely that health care is an unimportant component of the good life *tout court*. Perhaps they also understand subliminally that it is an unimportant determinant of health itself.

IX

There is more to health, of course, than a long life and a low infant mortality rate. There are many chronic complaints which do not threaten life directly but detract from the enjoyment of it, not only by the sufferer himself, but by those who surround him. There are some conditions, indeed, which cause suffering principally to the relatives of the person affected: Alzheimer's disease, for example. After the initial stages of this affliction, the person with the disease may not appreciate that there is anything wrong with him; but there are few more cruel or bitter ends to life than that in which the beloved husband, wife, father or mother dies, failing to recognise his or her own spouse and children, and reduced to a mere shell of his or her former self. The sometimes equivocal nature of medical progress is illustrated by the fact that the life expectancy of people diagnosed with Alzheimer's disease has increased in the last two decades from three or four years to about ten.* Is this entirely to be welcomed?

The measurement of human suffering is not a simple or straightforward matter, and attempts at comparison are fraught with difficulty. What is scarcely worthy of notice in one person or society may cause intense suffering in another. There is no doubt that acne, a vanishingly trivial condition from the point of view of mortality, can and does cause agonies of embarrassment, self-consciousness and depression among adolescents in a culture in which personal appearance is not merely important but some-times all-important; and in severe cases, the scarring and pitting of the skin may close off entire careers to the afflicted, and even affect the choice of marriage partner. Beauty is indeed only skin deep, but that is deep enough.

One cannot judge the degree of suffering merely by the severity of the condition which causes it; and comparisons made on this basis are, within quite wide limits, misleading. It is within the experience of every doctor that different

---

* The reasons for this increase are not entirely clear. It could be that old people are in general healthier than they were; or that there has been an improvement in the treatment of intercurrent illnesses such as pneumonia and angina; or even that the increase is the result of improved precision of diagnosis, inasmuch as the disease is now diagnosed earlier in its course and is more clearly differentiated from other diseases with a worse prognosis, such as arteriosclerotic multi-infarct dementia. Perhaps all three factors play a part.

groups of people react differently to the same illness. And every doctor who still makes house calls has been called up in the middle of the night for a completely trivial reason (a professional acquaintance of mine, for example, told me of how he had been called at three o'clock in the morning because his patient had run out of milk), yet also knows of cases in which a person in the last extremity has not called him until the very last minute for fear of inconveniencing him.

Ethnic, cultural and social groups differ in their tolerance of, and reaction to, illness, pain, distress and so forth. When I was a young doctor in Africa, I was impressed by the dignified stoicism of my patients. They tolerated in silence or with good humour what would have caused others to scream and protest in pain. They were capable of feats of endurance, even when old and ill, which would have been beyond the capacity of the fittest young athletes of other lands. Patients with fevers, injuries, anaemias or heart conditions, which elsewhere would have confined the sufferer strictly to bed, to be moved only on trolleys or stretchers, walked barefoot fifty miles through the bush to receive medical attention. (Here, if anywhere, Western medicine made the difference between life and death.) Trust in doctors to do their best was absolute; and if their best turned out to be not quite good enough, it was accepted without recrimination, without complaint and indeed with resignation.

Necessity is no doubt the mother of all stoicism, but there is no doubt either that stoicism is sometimes necessary and desirable. As to when precisely it *is* necessary and desirable, that – like everything else important in life – is a question of judgement. Stoicism in the face of a remediable cause of suffering is not to be wished, and may in fact be one of the principal causes of unnecessary suffering; but frantic activity in the face of the inevitable, with its implicit issue of false prospectuses, is another cause of unnecessary suffering.

In general, fortitude is not a quality which is much admired these days, because it is believed firstly that everyone is entitled to a life free of pain and distress, and that pain and distress are therefore deviations from the normal (in the ideal, if not the statistical, sense); and secondly that techniques exist in actuality for the alleviation of pain and distress whenever and in whatever circumstances it should occur. Fortitude is thus regarded as merely stupid, worthy of ridicule and even satire, rather than of admiration.

The cultural change which has brought about this reversal in the moral estimate of fortitude has been swift indeed. Observers during the Second World War were profoundly impressed by the general good humour and fortitude of the British people under the most difficult circumstances (it wasn't universal, of course, but it existed); and I remember a patient, a man whose life had not been by any means an easy one, who recalled his childhood during the war, in the course of which his home, a terraced house in a working-class district, was bombed.

'We lived in Albert Road,' he said, 'until Adolf Hitler moved us on.'

Until Adolf Hitler moved us on: what a wealth of fortitude is expressed in those few words, an ability to distance oneself from one's own suffering and, by doing so, to reduce its dimensions to manageable proportions, and even to laugh at it.

Nowadays, of course, it is more likely that a bombed-out family would try to sue the government for having got the country into such a mess in the first place; and counsellors would descend upon the unfortunates like vultures upon a carcass. There would be no recognition that the *meaning* of a trauma may serve to lessen or increase the intensity of the subsequent suffering (that the British were generally cheerful under bombardment because they believed themselves to be engaged on a great enterprise, namely that of saving freedom from tyranny and civilisation from barbarism, a belief which would be impossible for them now, since political correctness requires the use of inverted commas round the world civilisation, and in any case they are no longer in favour of it). This is why the expectation that life should pass without suffering serves paradoxically only to increase suffering, in so far as it reduces tolerance of it to zero.

In a psychotherapeutic world, there is no distress which cannot be eliminated or at least smoothed over by talking about it to strangers. Every misery has its simple corrective. The speed with which this sub-Freudian and quite baseless superstition has spread through the population is truly astonishing, for it scarcely existed twenty years ago except in the rarefied atmosphere of certain intellectual coteries; and my heart sinks whenever a patient confides in me that he thinks he needs counselling. The problems for which counselling is held to be the sovereign remedy range from bank robbery (curiously enough, always after capture, never at the planning stage) to failure to comply with medical treatment. The distinction between suffering which is self-inflicted and that which is the consequence of external circumstances is dissolved: because, strictly speaking, there is no suffering which is self-inflicted. Likewise the distinction between the world and representations of the world, already weakened by an almost universal addiction to television and video, is reduced almost to non-existence; for if a few sessions of talk with a stranger can make you whole, what evil can there be in the world except an insufficiency of counselling? If you continue to suffer after you have received such counselling, it must be because the counsellor was insufficiently skilful: another *casus belli* against life. And if for some reason you are refused the counselling which you believe will relieve your suffering, the true cause of your suffering is transferred from the circumstances which led to it to the unjust and cruel refusal. Suffering is not an inevitable part of life, with its losses and disappointments, but evidence that you are being denied something to which you are entitled.

There are no rights without duties, of course, and it is incumbent upon the person who is offered counselling to take it up (not to do so is the one instance in which suffering may be truly said to be self-inflicted). In some places, when a woman has a miscarriage she is routinely offered counselling; but if she refuses it on the grounds that she has a husband with whom to talk things over, and that, moreover, miscarriages are the kind of normal disappointment – up to half of all pregnancies end in miscarriage – with which anyone of reasonably firm disposition ought to be able to cope, she will not be praised or applauded for her fortitude, but rather accused implicitly of evading the issue, of laying herself open to later psychological problems, in short of failing in her duty to herself.

A patient of mine, a woman in middle age who worked part-time in a shop, was nearly strangled by one of three youths aged fourteen who had entered the shop intent upon stealing, and whom she had attempted to stop. She was left with bruises on her neck, proof of the force which the youth had used, who fortunately desisted before more serious physical damage was done. His associates laughed as he choked her, while also filling their pockets with the goods on display.

Somewhat unusually, the police caught the young criminals, who were let go with a warning (presumably that if they did it again they would receive another warning). The victim saw them the following day in the street, laughing and joking among themselves; and by the same day's post she received a letter from the police offering her counselling, to help her overcome the presumed effects of her recent unfortunate experience. It is curious in a psychotherapeutic age that the psychotherapeutic value of the just punishment of the perpetrators of such a crime should be so completely overlooked and vehemently denied; but what was peculiarly offensive to my patient about the offer of counselling was the implication that her anger and frustration that her near-strangulation should be dealt with so lightly by the state, and her consequent nervousness about living in a world in which potential murderers go scot-free after committing their assaults, were symptoms of neurosis, to be righted by talking for a few sessions to a complete stranger, rather than a reasonable response to the circumstances.

Thus the idea that all suffering is pathological leads in the end to the same failure to distinguish sensibly between avoidable and unavoidable suffering as the idea that, since all suffering is from God, it must all be borne with equal fatalism. The relativity of suffering imposes upon us the need for the constant exercise of judgement, whose elements include compassion, a sense of proportion, historical knowledge and an understanding of the limits of the possible.

X

The relativity of suffering notwithstanding, it is not unreasonable to suggest that the levels of physical discomfort experienced by people in the late twentieth century are hardly to be compared with those suffered by people of all earlier ages. It is possible to go further: almost no one in the world today (except under unusual political circumstances) suffers the kind of agonies which, until not so very long ago, were the common lot of mankind, from prince to pauper. Even in the remotest parts of the African bush, thanks to the existence of missionary hospitals, some kind of alleviation of prolonged agony is usually available, more effective in fact than any known to the most exalted only two centuries ago. The fact is that the great majority of people alive today in the advanced industrial countries (and most in many less advanced countries) will never experience in their entire lives the kind of physical suffering which was the lot of almost everyone to experience who survived childhood during the first few thousand years of human civilisation.

The comparative painlessness of modern life is so much taken for granted, and has become so 'natural', that it is almost beyond our powers of imagination to conceive of what life would be, or must have been, without the ability of modern medicine to alleviate and cure. Our forefathers

were without the benefit of local, let alone general, anaesthesia; and despite the proliferation of potentially dangerous machinery almost everywhere, we are much less liable
to accident than they. The simple life is not accident-free,
but on the contrary highly accident-prone. Numbers of
African children are burnt every year by wood fires, or
severely scalded by pulling the contents of cooking pots
over themselves; and those who till the soil with hand-held
implements are forever impaling themselves on them.
For most of mankind's history, the slightest injury, the
smallest break in the integrity of the skin, might rapidly
prove fatal.

Not only should the curative and palliative powers of
modern medical science have reduced our anxiety about
our health, but so should its explanatory powers. Even
when the specific cause of a disease is not yet known, the
explanatory framework of medical science is now so strong
that it is not unreasonable to suppose that the cause of the
disease will one day – in the not very distant future – be
found. The terror of phantasms which for so long dominated the human mind should long ago have evaporated.

The speed with which the cause of the AIDS epidemic
was elucidated stands in stark contrast with the millennium and a half, almost, which it took to understand the
cause of bubonic plague.* Indeed, the recognition that
AIDS *was* an epidemic was itself a triumph of modern
medicine, something whose astonishing nature is not often

---

* It is true to say that, at the time of the last great outbreak of plague in
Western Europe, in Marseilles in 1720, no more was known or understood of its real cause than during the plague of Justinian, in AD 542, or
during the Black Death of 1347–8, nearly twelve and four centuries
earlier respectively. Yersin and Kitasato discovered the plague bacillus
during an outbreak of the disease in Hong Kong in 1894.

acknowledged. Despite a few attempts to portray the disease as God's judgement upon homosexuals, heroin addicts, haemophiliacs and Haitians, the epidemic (which admittedly in North America and Western Europe is not to be compared in severity with previous epidemics of hitherto unknown diseases among susceptible populations, such as smallpox and measles among the Aztecs and Incas during the period of the Spanish conquest) did not call forth anything like the irrational manifestations which were common during epidemics of bubonic plague. And when a vaccine or a cure for AIDS is found, it is unlikely that a Santa Maria della Salute, the church in Venice built to commemorate and give thanks to God for the deliverance of the city from the plague epidemic of 1630, will be erected anywhere. A stage of human history has definitively been superseded.

In general, however, the comparatively rational approach to the causation of disease, far from liberating us from fear, has awakened new anxieties in us. Our ancestors feared intermittent strokes of punishment from God for our chronically unruly conduct, but we fear unseen enemies – soon to be unmasked by science itself – everywhere, enemies which lurk in the water we drink, in the air we breathe and in the food we eat. To this phenomenon I shall soon return.

First, though, it is necessary to give some idea of the physical suffering endured by those who came before us. There is such a large choice of testimony that I am forced to choose more or less at random from the books on medical history on the shelves of my study.

Philip II of Spain was probably the most powerful monarch in the world of his time. His was the original empire upon which the sun never set. Despite his power, despite the fact that he could command obedience from millions of subjects, his final illness and death, in 1598, were horrible. Here is an account of his final two months of existence:*

On 22 July, Philip was carried to his bed for the last time. Around midnight, he developed a high fever that signalled the beginning of a long, agonising demise. . .

For the next fifty-three days Philip was forced to lie flat on his back, unable to move and unable to be moved or touched without pain. Even the weight of the sheets caused him distress. The gout and arthritis that had plagued him for the past few years continued to torment him and may even have intensified. The dreaded *tercianas* fever caused him to alternate between hot flashes and chills. The sores on his hands and feet also worsened and had to be lanced. He developed a festering abscess above his right knee that also had to be lanced without the aid of any anesthetic on 6 August. This open wound would not drain properly and had to be squeezed, yielding two basins full of pus each day. Philip's chronic dropsy caused his abdomen and joints to swell with fluid. Bed sores erupted all along his backside as the ordeal progressed. Although at times he lapsed into a fitful sleep or seemed barely conscious, he was troubled by insomnia and never fully escaped from the horror of his condition.

According to all eyewitnesses, the worst torment of

* I quote Carlos M.N. Eire, *From Madrid to Purgatory*, Cambridge University Press, 1996.

all was the diarrhoea that developed about halfway
into his final illness. Because the pain caused by being
touched or moved was too great for Philip to bear, it
seemed best not to clean the ordure that he produced,
and not even to change his linens, so many times the
bed remained fouled, creating an awful stench.
Eventually a hole was cut into the mattress to help
relieve this problem, but it was only a partial remedy.
Philip continued to waste away, wallowing in his own
filth, tormented by the smell and the degradation of it
all. According to one account, he was also plagued by
lice.

No one dies like this nowadays, let alone those who have
the power to command the best of everything that is available.

Just over two centuries later, in 1810, the novelist Fanny
Burney, then living in Paris, discovered that she had a
tumour of the breast. At first she tried to ignore it, but
finally agreed to have an operation. This is how the operation went:

Dr. Moreau instantly entered my room, to see if I were
alive. He gave me wine cordial & went to the salon. I
rang for my Maid & Nurses, – but before I could
speak to them, my room, without previous message,
was entered by seven men in black, Dr. Larry, M.
Dubois, Dr. Moreau, Dr. Aumont, Dr. Ribe, & a pupil
of Dr. Larry & another of M. Dubois. I was now awakened from my stupor – & by sort of indignation – why
so many? & why without leave? – But I could not
utter a syllable. M. Dubois acted as Commander in
Chief. Dr. Larry kept out of sight; M. Dubois ordered

a Bed stead into middle of the room. Astonished, I
turned to Dr. Larry, who had promised that an Arm
chair would suffice; but he hung his head, & would
not look at me. Two *old mattresses* M. Dubois then
demanded & an old sheet. I now began to tremble
violently, more with distaste and horrour of prepara-
tions even than of the pain. These arranged to his
liking, he desired me to mount the Bed stead. I stood
suspended, for a moment, whether I should not
abruptly escape – I looked at the door, the windows –
I felt desperate – but it was only for a moment, my
reason then took command, & my fears & feeling
struggled vainly against it. I called to my maid – she
was crying, & the two nurses stood transfixed to the
door. Let those women all go! cried M. Dubois. This
order recovered me my voice – No, I cried, let them
stay! *qu'elles restent*! This occasioned a little dispute,
that re-animated me – The Maid, however, and one of
the nurses ran off – I charged the other to approach,
& she obeyed. M. Dubois now tried to issue his
commands *en militaire*, but I resisted all that were
resistable – I was compelled, however, to submit to
taking off my long robe de Chambre, which I had
meant to retain . . . I mounted, therefore, unbidden,
the Bed stead – & M. Dubois placed me upon the
mattress, & spread a cambric handkerchief over my
face. It was transparent, however, & I saw, through it
that the Bed stead was instantly surrounded by the 7
men & my nurse, I refused to be held; but when,
bright through the cambric, I saw the glitter of
polished Steel – I closed my Eyes. I would not trust to
convulsive fear the sight of the terrible incision. A
silence most profound ensued, which lasted for some

minutes, during which, I imagine, they took their orders by signs, & made their examination – Oh what horrible suspension! – I did not breathe – & M. Dubois tried vainly to find any pulse. This pause, at length was broken by Dr. Larry, who in a voice solemn melancholy, said 'qui me tendra ce sein?' – No one answered; at least not verbally; but this aroused me from my passively submissive state, for I feared they imagined the whole breast infected – feared it too justly, – for, again through the Cambric, I saw the hand of M. Dubois held up, while his forefinger first described a straight line from top to bottom of the breast, secondly a Cross, & thirdly a circle; intimating that the whole was to be taken off. Excited by this idea, I started up, threw off my veil, &, in answer to his demand 'Qui me tendra ce sein?' cried 'C'est moi, Monsieur!' & I held my hand under it, & explained the nature of my sufferings, which all sprang from one point, though they darted into every part. I was heard attentively, but in utter silence, & M. Dubois then replaced me as before, &, as before spread my veil over my face. How vain, alas, my representation! immediately again I saw the fatal finger describe the Cross – & the circle – Hopeless, then desperate, & self-given up, I closed once more my Eyes, relinquishing all watching, all resistance, all interference, & sadly resolute to be wholly resigned.

. . . [T]his resolution once taken, was firmly adhered to, in defiance of a terror that surpasses all description, & the most torturing pain. Yet – when the dreadful steel was plunged into the breast – cutting through veins – arteries – flesh – nerves – I needed no injunctions not to restrain my cries. I began a scream that lasted unintermittingly during the whole time of the incision – & I almost marvel that it rings not in my Ears still! so excruciating was the agony! When the wound was made, the instrument was withdrawn, the pain seemed undiminished, for the air that rushed into those delicate parts felt like a mass of minute but sharp & forked poniards, that were tearing the edges of the wound, – but when again I felt the instrument – describing a curve – cutting against the grain, if I may so say, while the flesh resisted in a manner so forcible as to oppose & tire the hand of the operator, who was forced to change from the right to the left – then, indeed, I thought I must have expired, I attempted no more to open my Eyes, – they felt as if hermettically shut, & so firmly closed, that the Eyelids seemed indented into the Cheeks, the Instrument this second time withdrawn, I concluded the operation over – Oh no! presently the terrible cutting was renewed – & worse than ever, to separate the bottom, the foundation of this terrible gland from the parts to which it adhered – Again all description would be baffled – yet again all was not over, Dr. Larry rested but his own hand, & oh Heaven! – I then felt the Knife rackling against the breast bone – scraping it! – This performed, while I yet remained in utterly speechless torture, I heard the Voice of M. Larry, – (all others guarded a dead silence) in a tone nearly tragic, desire every one present to pronounce if anything more remained to be done; The general voice was Yes – but the finger of Mr. Dubois – which I literally *felt* elevated over the wound, though I saw nothing, & though he touched nothing, so indescribably sensitive was the spot – pointed to some further requisition – & again began the scraping! – and, after this, Dr. Moreau thought he discerned a peccant attom – and still, & still, M. Dubois demanded attom after attom – . . . not for Weeks, but for Months I could not speak of this terrible business without nearly going through it!. . .

To conclude, the evil was so profound, the case so delicate, & the precautions necessary for preventing a return so numerous, that the operation, including the treatment & the dressing, lasted 20 minutes! . . . When all was done, & they lifted me up that I might be put to bed, my strength was so totally annihilated, that I was obliged to be carried, and could not even sustain my hands & arms; which hung as if I had been lifeless; while my face, as the Nurse has told me, was utterly colourless. This removal made me open my Eyes – & then I saw my good Dr. Larry, pale nearly as myself, his face streaked with blood, & its expression depicting grief, apprehension, and almost horrour.

One trembles just to read this account. The worst of hospital horror stories today, which newspapers delight to relay to a neurotic public, can hardly begin to match the horror of Fanny Burney's operation, which was *routine* for the time. What is unusual about her case is that she survived to tell the tale, and that she had the talent to do so. The vast majority of those operated upon left no such record of their sufferings.

It might be argued, of course, that Philip II and Fanny Burney were worse off in some respects than the poor of their time, who could not have afforded the medical attention which they received, and therefore might have been spared some of the pain inflicted by medical practitioners upon them. The sufferings of Philip II and Fanny Burney were not typical of their era, but worse than typical.

But the poor of previous centuries were not entirely deprived of medical attention, which was unlikely to have been of a better quality than that available to this privileged pair. The pages of the Victorian *Lancet* are replete with medical stories to make the blood run cold, a very small percentage of which could have come to public attention. It was not uncommon, for example, for accoucheurs to remove not only the afterbirth during a delivery, but the entire uterus and even pieces of intestine, the patient dying horribly an hour or two later.

XI

Not all the statistics in the world, however, and not all the contemplation of the sufferings of those unfortunate enough to have been born before us, are sufficient to allay our anxieties about ourselves, or to persuade us that we have nothing much to worry about, that we should get on with our lives in peace and serenity.

Perhaps the most immediate cause of our unprecedented, and unprecedentedly unnecessary, concern with our health is the eagerness with which the media of mass communication take up the latest findings of epidemiological research, magnify them and then use them to imply that the individual, or the government, or both, should take immediate action based upon them.*

The usual method adopted is as follows. Researchers, needing some new subject to keep the research funds flowing, study a comparatively rare disease – cancer of the pancreas, shall we say, to take a real and recent example – and discover that those who suffer from it have drunk more coffee during their lifetimes than those of the same age, sex, social class and type of employment who do not. The report appears in a prestigious and unimpeachable medical journal – the *New England Medical Journal*, shall we say, or *The Lancet* – and, because coffee is an article of almost universal consumption, the report is deemed to be of urgent interest to millions of newspapers readers and television viewers, who naturally enough draw the conclusion that, if you don't want to get cancer of the pancreas, you'd better give up drinking coffee.

There is much which can be said about this kind of research, its chain of inferences and the panics to which it gives rise.

The first is that most of the researchers who undertake it hope to find something important from the public health point of view. The conception of scientific research as driven by a disinterested thirst for the Truth is false, or at

---

* No sooner was it publicised that the British diet was deficient in selenium, which might account for Britain's comparatively high rates of cancer and heart attack, than the government was asked to formulate a policy concerning selenium in the British diet; meanwhile, brazil nuts, supposedly of high selenium content, disappeared from the supermarkets. Needless to say, those who bought the nuts in a panic were the section of the population least at risk of suffering prematurely from cancer or heart attack. Ironically, the vitamin E pills which the same people had for some time been swallowing to avoid the same diseases were soon afterwards declared in the newspapers to be not merely ineffective, but possibly dangerous.

least incomplete. Like all others who publish, scientists hope for public notice, recognition and even for immortality. Hence it is only natural for them to study items of universal consumption in the hope of finding a connection with one disease or another, for then they are assured of a little of the limelight which millions of us secretly crave, because limelight reassures us that our lives are not without some importance or transcendent significance.

Coffee is thus an excellent object of research, certain to capture the public interest, and indeed it has been implicated in the production of heart attacks and early miscarriages of pregnancy. Boiled coffee in particular is thought to raise levels of cholesterol in the blood.

It must be borne in mind that alleged associations such as that between drinking coffee and cancer of the pancreas are presented in terms of their *statistical* significance. This does not mean that the association is significant in any other way, still less that there is a causative relationship between the two. It simply means that, according to certain mathematical principles, the association is unlikely to have arisen by chance alone. By convention – and it *is* a convention – such an association is said to be statistically significant if there is a less than 5 per cent chance of it having arisen by chance.

There is, of course, an almost infinitely large number of conditions to which flesh is heir which can be studied in this fashion; moreover, there is also an indefinitely large number of factors which may have a statistical association with each of these conditions. In short, there is a virtually infinite number of possible factors which may be associated with disease.

In fact, the greater the number of diseases which are studied, and the larger the number of factors examined, the larger the number of associations which will be found that appear not to have arisen by chance but in fact have done so. Thus, if a hundred possibly disease-associated factors are examined with respect to a certain disease, some of them will inevitably be found to be statistically associated with that disease – a fact which reflects upon the nature of statistics rather than of the disease. Indeed, the number of associations between disease and factors in the environment which appear not to have arisen by chance when in fact they have done so is itself infinite.

The number of potential health panics is therefore likewise enormous, and for all practical purposes without limit (one can usually panic about only one or two things at a time, however, which means that even in an entire lifetime of acute anxiety, one will never have succeeded in panicking over any but a tiny proportion of possible matters for panic).

Since the end of the Second World War, with the virtual extinction of infectious diseases as a cause of premature death, epidemiologists – who until then were few, and until then principally studied epidemics or epidemic disease – had to find something else to do. The association game offered not only the possibility of infinitely long periods of employment (the subject matter could never be exhausted), but provided a justification for an enormous expansion of the epidemiological infrastructure. The numbers of people working in epidemiology increased at precisely the time when they were the least necessary; but since they had, from the institutional and career points of view, to publish *something*, they at once set about finding associations.

Not surprisingly, most medical journals prefer to publish positive rather than negative results. If the researchers who originally investigated the hypothetical link between consumption of coffee and cancer of the pancreas had found that there was, in fact, no such statistical association, it is unlikely that they would have found any journal – or any *celebrated* journal, for medical journals have themselves, like epidemiologists, proliferated, and one can always be found to publish what others reject – to publish this rather uninteresting finding, because no one had supposed in the first place that there was any such association. If the eating of peaches were associated with the contracting of multiple sclerosis, we would soon enough get to hear of it; but if it were not, we should never even know that the purported association had been considered and examined.

Once a positive finding has been published, however, there is always room for the publication of further negative findings, precisely because the possibility of a positive association has been raised. But just as the original positive finding might have arisen by chance, so might the subsequent negative ones. Furthermore, the follow-up studies rarely duplicate the methods of the initial study completely; and thus there is room for debate as to whether the difference in the results is because of the way the world is, or because of the different methods in studying it. By hook or by crook there is always room, and justification, for further research.

There comes a point, of course, when it is accepted that the original positive association – say, that between green potatoes and the birth of babies with spina bifida – was spurious. But that is not quite the end of the matter, because the publicity given to the original observation leaves a trace in the minds of millions of people; for not only are the subsequent negative findings never given the same publicity as the original positive ones, cause for panic being news while cause for peace of mind is not, but there is an almost universal human tendency to believe that there is no smoke without fire.* For a considerable time, therefore, confidence in the safety of an item of daily consumption is destroyed; and either consumption falls, with unfortunate effects upon those who labour in the industry which produces that item, or the consumers feel a certain guilt at their own irresponsibility at consuming something which they think they know is bad for their health.

Moreover, a non-specific anxiety soon takes hold of the mind about the world in general. Coffee has been drunk for hundreds of years, yet no one until now has noticed that it caused a fatal disease, namely cancer of the pancreas. If such a thing could have been overlooked for so long, how many other dangers might (or must) there be lurking in what we previously had considered safe, in our trusting and unthinking fashion?

Indeed, the more we consume, the more such hazards there must be. It isn't only food and drink which threaten us; it is the increasing sophistication of the instruments which we use in our daily lives. Microwave ovens cause cancer, video and computer screens cause cancer, mobile telephones cause brain tumours. The list of dangers already discovered and yet to be discovered is endless.

Compared with the modern world, then, with all its

* Paranoia never lies very deep below the 'surface' of the human mind. It is curious how large a number of structural or metabolic alterations in the human body result in paranoia, as if it had been bubbling away all the time under the lid of civilised consciousness, rather as barbarism is said to lie under a surface of cultural refinement. No doubt there is an evolutionary explanation of Man's propensity for paranoia; but even if there is, it does not invalidate the value of reason and civilisation, which are all we have to protect us from madness and barbarity.

hazardous chemicals (over a hundred in cigarette smoke alone!) and secret deadly rays emanating from our tools around us, the world of the mediaeval witchfinder was simple indeed. At least all the evil then existent was attributable to but a few malefactors, acting under the direction of the Devil. Defeat, or frustrate, the Devil and all would be well; but who can fight on so many fronts at once, against deadly rays, against carcinogens, against contamination, against food preservatives, against hormones and anti-hormones in food, water and plastic food wrappings, against overpopulation and declining sperm counts, against secret allergens and viruses yet to be discovered and not even suspected to exist? Never was the world so dangerous; never was there so much to worry about.

The purity of the world is lost. We forget that, actually, the world was never very pure. Hence Swift's graphic poem after a shower of rain in London in 1710:

> Sweepings from butchers stalls, dung, guts, and
>   blood,
> Drowned puppies, stinking sprats, all drenched in
>   mud,
> Dead cats and turnip-tops come tumbling down
>   the flood.

We forget that, nearly a century and a half later, the River Aire in Leeds was described as follows:

> It was full of refuse from water closets, cesspools, privies, common drains, dung-hill drainings, infirmary refuse, wastes from slaughter houses, chemical soap, gas, dye-houses, and manufacturers, coloured by blue and black dye, pig manure, old urine wash;

there were dead animals, vegetable substances and occasionally a decomposed human body.

We forget that Victorian food – at a time when the health of the population was improving – was grossly contaminated, that strychnine was put in rum, copper sulphate in pickles, bottled fruit, wine and preserves, lead chromate in mustard and snuff, ferrous sulphate in tea and beer, ferric ferrocyanide in Chinese tea, copper carbonate, lead sulphate and bisulphate of mercury in sugar and chocolate, red lead in Gloucester cheese, and arsenates in green paper to wrap food and the coloration of wallpapers. We forget that in 1855 *Punch* ran a cartoon in which a little girl approaches a grocer and says, 'If you please, sir, mother says, will you let her have a quarter of a pound of your best tea to kill the rats with, and an ounce of chocolate as would get rid of the black beadles [beetles].'

We forget that in 1862 a third of all butchers' meat was found to come from animals which had died of disease; that in 1871 a quarter of milk sold was found to be adulterated with water or chalk, or both; that 10 per cent of the butter, 8 per cent of the bread and 50 per cent of the gin sold were adulterated with copper; and that late Victorian ice-cream contained, *inter alia*, cocci, bacilli, cotton fibre, lice, bedbugs, fleas, and human, cat and dog hair.

No, we prefer to surround ourselves with dangers which we fondly suppose are unprecedented both in scope and in severity.

XII

It is repeated on innumerable occasions that a statistical association does not imply cause and effect. But the very fact that this wise dictum has to be repeated so many times, like a Spanish royal decree regarding the gentle treatment of Indians in the American empire, suggests that people have some difficulty in remembering it, or at least in putting it into practice. *Obedezco pero no cumplo*, as Spanish colonial officials used to say on receiving further humanitarian instructions from Spain – I obey but I do not fulfil.

Even those who have constantly warned against the self-denying and puritanical ordinances of health fanatics, which are more often than not predicated upon precisely such epidemiological associations, forget their own principles when – at long last – an association emerges which pleases them, and is taken to prove that a pleasure of the flesh is not only pleasant and innocent in itself, but positively healthful. Thus, when it was reported in the medical press that those who drank alcohol in moderation had longer life expectancies, and died less frequently from heart attacks, than either those who never drank at all or who drank to excess, no time was lost in recommending that people should drink for the sake of their health. This recommendation only made sense if the relationship between moderate drinking and longevity were a causative one; and while it is possible to hypothesise why it should be so, it is equally possible to hypothesise why it should not be so (for example, it could be moderation *per se* which is life-preserving, teetotallers being enthusiasts of supposed virtue). Certainly, the recommendations preceded proof by a long way, while the habitual nay-sayers, by contrast, fell silent, as the mere possibility that something pleasurable might actually be good for the health threatened to blow up their entire *Weltanschauung*.

Recently in Colombia, I read a newspaper article which suggested that regular sexual intercourse was good for the health. I believe that similar articles have appeared elsewhere. The idea of indulging in sexual intercourse for the same reason as one mounts an exercise bicycle is intriguing, to say the least, and raises the possibility, I suppose, of health brothels. Two days after this article was published, I was handed a condom in the street of a remote town by a passing procession of health workers, who were bringing the attention of the no doubt ill-informed townsfolk to the dangers of AIDS. The combined message seemed to be, then, to have sex often but to remain anxious about it. This is the modern equivalent of the Welsh Baptist preacher who, when asked whether it was permissible to have sex on Sundays, replied, 'Yes, so long as you don't enjoy it.' I suspect that the local population was more susceptible to the first than to the second half of the advice, and quite rightly so.

Statistical associations may be quite strong, and yet be of little or no aetiological significance. I have noticed, for example, two associations with serious crime in Britain which are very strong, but which are unlikely to have much by way of explanatory power. These associations are that virtually 100 per cent of white British criminals are tattooed, and that the same proportion of them smoke.

Even when controlled for the class from which most criminals are drawn, the association is still a very strong one. Let us suppose that 50 per cent of young males at liberty of that class smoke and are tattooed: the fact that 98 per cent of their incarcerated contemporaries likewise smoke and are tattooed must then achieve a high degree of statistical significance. What is the explanation for these strong statistical associations?

It would, of course, be possible to put forward hypotheses of causation. Perhaps the tattooing needle introduces a virus which, years later, finds its way into the brain and there wreaks subtle havoc which results in criminal behaviour. It is no objection that not every such tattooed person becomes a criminal – or indeed that the vast majority do not – first because it is possible that the tattooing needle introduces the virus into only a small percentage of the tattooed, and second because it is well known that not everyone reacts to viruses in the same way. Of people infected with the viruses of hepatitis B and C, for example, only 20 to 30 per cent go on to develop chronic liver disease, so that a precedent for such variability in response already exists. There is no disease condition, in fact, for whose development the presence of a viral, bacterial or parasitic organism is both a necessary and sufficient condition.

And who is to say that a virus could not or cannot act in this selective way? It has long been suspected that psychopathy, that condition called *moral insanity* by the English alienist of the first half of the nineteenth century Dr Prichard, because the sufferer lacked both a sense of morality and the ability to learn from the consequences of that lack, is actually a physical condition of the brain, caused by a shortage of oxygen at birth, a perinatal infection, or some such subtle and hitherto undetectable influence. Sophisticated techniques of brain imaging have – allegedly – shown differences in the functioning of the brains of psychopaths on the one hand and normal moral law-abiding citizens on the other.

Even if the evidence did not lend intrinsic plausibility to the viral theory of crime, it would still be necessary to retain a certain modesty in the face of the facts; for the association between crime and tattooing must be explained somehow, and it would be wrong to rule out possibilities *a priori*. The correct idea that infectious diseases were caused by organisms invisible to the naked eye was propounded hundreds of years before it was proved correct, but was rejected precisely because it could not be proved, and there was no analogy with any known mechanism of the causation of disease. *Eppur si muove*.

As for cigarettes, it is known that nicotine has physiological and psychological effects. (A criminal's consumption of cigarettes, incidentally, precedes his incarceration rather than follows it, and is therefore not a consequence of it.)* Schizophrenics likewise smoke, almost to a man or woman, independently of where they live, whether it be an asylum or a wretched lodging in a slum. And it is no

* The *Sunday Telegraph*, 8 December, 1996 – an edition further cited below – reported a study carried out on teenagers which found that teenage 'hardened' smokers were up to twenty times more likely than non-smokers to try illegal drugs; and since illegal drug-taking is closely associated with the commission of other kinds of crime, smoking is thus linked to crime. On the basis of these figures, there was an immediate call by enthusiasts for a ban on all cigarette advertising, no one noticing – apparently – that there were a few intermediate steps between the disappearance of such advertising and the disappearance of burglary, mugging and murder.

objection that only a tiny minority of smokers turn to crime – unless smoking be considered a crime in itself – for it is well known that psychoactive substances, alcohol included, affect people differently. Marijuana may be smoked, and amphetamines taken by a variety of routes, in large quantities by many people without any falling prey to paranoia; but in a few people this reaction follows.

A causative mechanism can always be hypothesised to explain an association, for the number of possible hypotheses to explain a phenomenon, like the number of phenomena, is infinite. And this being so, it is inevitable that, as soon as an association is mentioned, a causative relationship is assumed to exist. For example, no sooner is it demonstrated statistically that heart attacks are more frequent in areas in which the water supply is soft rather than hard than people suppose that heart attacks are caused by soft water. They are then presented with a typical late-twentieth-century moral dilemma: whether it is better to live with soft water in which soap dissolves easily, or with hard water which conduces to cardiac health.

The deficiencies of associationist epidemiology were clearly exhibited during the first stages of the AIDS epidemic. Before very long, the pattern of transmission of the immune deficiency (itself a brilliant unifying explanation of phenomena as different as Kaposi's sarcoma and pneuomocystis carinii pneumonia, which until then were extremely rare in young men) began strikingly to resemble that of hepatitis B. Until then, however, the lives and habits of the sufferers were examined with a fine-tooth comb, it having been forgotten that the larger the number of factors examined, the more red herrings (to change the metaphor slightly) were bound to be caught. Many false hypotheses were raised, the principal among them being that AIDS was caused by the rectal consumption of glyceryl nitrite by promiscuous homosexuals.

A modified version of this theory is still adhered to by the maverick scientist Professor Peter Duesberg, who has attained an immense notoriety because of his rejection of the generally accepted viewpoint. He claims that the presence of the Human Immunodeficiency Virus (HIV) in sufferers from AIDS is a consequence rather than a cause of the disease, and that the virus is harmless in itself. He subjects the HIV theory of the causation of AIDS to searching criticism, pointing out every last discrepancy and contradiction in the evidence; but his own theory is based on the crudest of epidemiological associationism, complete with graphs showing the simultaneous increase in drug addiction and in the number of cases of AIDS, without realising that a very similar comparison could be made with the possession of personal computers, or no doubt a host of other supposed factors. It is nonetheless true that, if only a tiny fraction of the immense sums devoted to reasearch on AIDS had been devoted to a few decisive experiments, Professor Duesberg's theory could have been refuted once and for all. No doubt his somewhat paranoid manner of expressing himself, claiming that AIDS research is dominated by ambitious and unscrupulous virologists who are determined to scoop research funds for themselves, and to hog the limelight, has not helped his cause. Whether this *ad hominem* manner of argumentation, common in private but not in scientific discourse, is the cause or consequence of his treatment by the scientific community is a question which future historians of science will have to answer for themselves – according to the interests of their own careers, no doubt.

Associationist epidemiology draws its sustenance and

prestige from an early triumph, the demonstration in 1952 by Sir Richard Doll of the link between smoking and lung cancer. It is generally accepted by scientists that this link is a causative one, though even here there have been sceptics as eminent as Professor Eysenck, who argued that the kind of person who smoked cigarettes was precisely the kind of person who contracted lung cancer, and that it was the personality of the smoking sufferer, rather than the smoke, which caused the cancer. Perhaps it will not come altogether as a surprise to readers to learn that Professor Eysenck devised and developed one of the most widely used multiple-choice questionnaires to measure personality. It is called a personality *inventory*, the same word used for listing the contents of an apartment or house when it is rented out.

Epidemiologists the world over no doubt dream of repeating the cigarette triumph.* Such a repeat would assure them of fame and immortality at a stroke. But there are two important lessons from the cigarette story which are often overlooked. The first is that, for epidemiological research to yield useful rather than harmful results, inasmuch as false alarms lead to panic and result in irrational behaviour, it should be inspired by a specific question posed by clinical science, rather than be a trawl more or less at random through the great ocean of hitherto unexamined

---

* Actually, it was German doctors under the Nazis who first established the link between smoking and cancer, but it is not polite to mention it, especially as the measures taken by the Nazis against smoking were precisely the same ones as are recommended today by anti-smoking campaigners. The Luftwaffe banned smoking in 1938, and the Nazi party followed suit in its offices in 1939. In 1943 it was made illegal for anyone under eighteen to smoke in public, and in 1944 Hitler was said to be so worried about the exposure of young female bus conductors to tobacco smoke that smoking was banned on city buses and trains.

possible risk factors.* It hardly requires much thought (at least, once it is pointed out) to see that lung cancer and the repeated and habitual drawing into the lungs of smoke containing large numbers of organic compounds might be connected in a causative way. Whereas such a connection between the recent rise in the incidence of asthma and the importation of tropical fruit into the country would be rather more difficult (though perhaps not impossible) to envisage; for all I know the association between the two is highly significant from the statistical point of view. Obviously, further research is called for – funded, of course, by the taxpayer.

The second lesson from the cigarette–lung cancer triumph is the hazard of making direct international comparisons. Had the original research been done using international statistics, the connection between lung cancer and smoking might well have been missed, or at least its strength under-estimated. The British have (or had) the highest rate of lung cancer in the world, but their consumption of cigarettes is by no means the greatest. As is well known, the Japanese smoke furiously, but their rate of lung cancer is low.

---

* That panic can easily be sown and result in harmful policies was pointed out by the surgeon Wilfred Trotter in the early days of the Second World War. He wrote:

> A total black-out was enforced without compromise or graduation or any provision for the devoted pedestrian. The consequences may well become a classical example of the staggering paradoxes that result from mixing good intentions with panic. Deaths by violence on the roads rose in the first month of the war from 500 to 1,100. Thus by sitting quietly at home Hitler's air force was able to kill 600 British citizens at a cost to itself of exactly nothing.

Incidentally, there figures demonstrate the relative safety of modern life. Although the number of vehicles on Britain's roads has increased tenfold since Trotter's day, the number of people killed on the roads has declined by half.

This does not mean that lung cancer is not caused by smoking, however. Even among the Japanese, a strong association exists between lung cancer and smoking. It simply means that, in an organism as complex as Man, one factor rarely explains everything. Smoking is nearly, but not quite, a necessary condition for the development of lung cancer, but it is clearly not sufficient. If you don't smoke, you are unlikely to die of lung cancer, but it is not impossible that you will do so.

In short, neither the presence nor absence of a statistical association is sufficient in medicine to establish the causation of disease. At the most, an association may guide us as to where to look for a cause; but the cause itself must be established by experimental methods.

Therefore, send not for the selenium pills. They may do you no good; they may even do you harm. And the bell will toll for you anyway.

XIII

Increasingly, associationist epidemiology acts as a powerful stimulant to one of the least attractive of human appetites: the appetite for effortless gain on the largest possible scale.

Perhaps it is not altogether surprising (in an age when more people than ever before in human history, and possibly even a majority of the population now living, will survive to a ripe old age without serious mishap befalling them which cannot be cured or alleviated by modern medicine, until their final illness) that accidents which were once regarded as a natural and inevitable concomitant of life itself are seen as legally actionable. If we are all entitled to a life free of illness and injury, then – when illness or injury occurs – we must be entitled to compensation. Shakespeare said that gold can make black white and bad good; these days, just the hope of compensation can perform even more amazing feats of transformation.

The hope of compensation can, for example, conjure suffering out of satisfaction, almost instantaneously at that. Until the *New England Journal of Medicine* published an article suggesting a link between silicone breast implants and the development of serious autoimmune connective tissue diseases such as scleroderma and dermatomyositis, most of the two million women in America who had received such an implant had – according to surveys carried out – expressed their satisfaction with them. No sooner had the article appeared, however, than the writs began to fly. For if the women who had undergone the implants were being made ill by them, the manufacturer must be to blame and therefore had to pay.

This is not the place to comment on a society in which so large a number of women have submitted to a serious operation for purely cosmetic reasons (only a fifth of the women had their implants to replace breast tissue lost in operations for cancer): no doubt feminists can make that particular hay. But what is striking is that people nowadays imagine that operations of an unprecedented nature can be performed entirely without risk to themselves of long-term damage, and indeed that it can be known in advance of all experience what those risks – if any – are. The principle of buyer beware has been replaced in its entirety by the principle of seller beware: the customer really can do no wrong.

Enormous sums in damages were claimed from the manufacturers, who agreed to pay $4.25 thousand million (of which a thousand million was set aside for the lawyers), an amount which many of the plaintiffs found quite inadequate. Aggressive lawyers, eager for business, touted for clients who believed themselves to be ill as a result of their implants; and it is a fair bet that, with the prospect of huge sums of money dancing before their eyes (one settlement alone was for $10 million), substantial numbers of women with breast implants who until then had felt perfectly well began to feel unwell, and to suffer from innumerable vague, ill-defined yet pervasive symptoms. This is not to say they were guilty of conscious fraud, though some of them may have been. It is simply that, once alerted to the possibility that they were ill, and that if they were they might receive a lot of money, they attended more carefully to their bodily sensations, recorded them assiduously and interpreted them more pessimistically than they had done before, as a man who has had a cancer removed interprets a twinge in his abdomen differently from a man who has never had a day's illness in his life. Unselfconsciousness is like the bloom of the grape: one touch, and it is gone for good, never to return. Besides, it has been amply demonstrated – by the British system of social security, for example – that if you pay people to be sick, they will be sick. The self-employed are not incapacitated by those things which incapacitate employees. And just as invalidity benefit calls forth invalids, like a rabbit out of a magician's hat, so the prospect of compensation calls forth the very injury for which it is supposedly the compensation.

In the case of silicone breast implants and connective tissue disorders, the only prima-facie case for a causative link was a statistical association between the two. It is true that experimental scientists began then to provide plausible reasons as to why there should be such a link, but in this instance the case fell or stood by the reproducibility and strength of the statistical association.

Subsequent attempts to demonstrate such an association have not succeeded; and it is now the generally accepted view among experts that there is at present no good reason to suppose that silicone breast implants cause connective tissue diseases. This has not in the least prevented the cases from going ahead, or huge awards from being made. For no amount of research, of course, can ever prove a negative beyond all possible doubt. Further research might yet prove positive.

Unfortunately, the fact that silicone breast implants have not so far been proved unsafe is not a matter for rejoicing for many of the women who have had them, far from it. Those women who felt ill as a result of hearing about the harm which their implants might have done them continue to feel unwell, for if their symptoms abated with the latest failure of researchers to corroborate the original research, they would have to acknowledge to themselves that they had been engaged, in effect, upon a massive fraud, or that at the very least they were the victims of mass hysteria.

Those who succeeded in their claims, and received sums of money from the manufacturers, will probably find it difficult ever to recover, for were they to do so they would then know that they had been mere extortionists (ably assisted by corrupt lawyers); while those who received no compensation will feel cheated of their due, and thus turn themselves into victims of injustice, perpetrated by large corporations. Will not the fact that they continue to feel unwell be proof in itself that they deserve some recompense, in fact a far larger sum than they would ever have been able to accumulate in any other way?

Thus the hope of compensation conjured hypochondriacal blackmailers out of perfectly normal and no doubt decent people.*

The entire sorry saga of the silicone breast implant case – with billions of dollars paid in lawyers' fees and unjustified compensation for imaginary injury, tens of thousands of women made to feel unwell either from anxiety or from the hope of gain, and the Dow-Corning Corporation obliged to seek protection from its creditors – was created by a single example of an epidemiological association: an association which, even had it been substantiated, would not necessarily have meant what it was precipitately taken to mean by those with axes to grind and fortunes to make.

XIV

Statistical association is not the only means by which unnecessary anxieties may be, and are, raised and maintained. Toxicological science is a powerful stimulus to perpetual panic.

* In Britain, there seems to be a tendency of late for claims against hospitals and doctors to be settled out of court, irrespective of the merits of the case being brought. This is because it is cheaper to settle in this manner and lose than win in open court. Since the costs of the claimant are usually paid out of public funds, and nothing is recoverable from him by a successful defendant, the fraudulent litigant has nothing to lose by making his claim. The effect of such a system upon the character of people who are aware of its existence may readily be imagined. He who pays the Danegeld never gets rid of the Dane.

It having been decided that the caffeine in coffee was bad for health, it seemed perfectly natural that decaffeinated coffee should be produced. In some circles, taking decaffeinated coffee came for a time to be almost a visible sign of moral election. I recall an application form for a conference (about how doctors should deal with abusive patients without alienating them), the attendance fee to include 'non-caffeinated refreshments' (as well as vegetarian food), smugness radiating from every word.

All too predictably, an alarm was soon sounded about the safety of decaffeinated coffee. Those who had avoided caffeine to protect their hearts were hoist with their own petard: as hypochondriacs generally are, sooner or later. It was suggested that the chemicals by means of which coffee is decaffeinated were themselves carcinogenic. The only good coffee was no coffee.

The evidence on which the allegations of danger were based was not strong; but in matters such as these, it doesn't have to be strong to achieve its effect. After all, you only live once, so when it comes to fatal illness you can't play too safe.

Mice were dosed with the chemicals which are used in the decaffeination of coffee and – lo and behold! – they developed cancer of the stomach in larger than expected numbers. Extrapolating with near-poetic licence, the press soon alerted the public to the danger lurking in its cups and mugs.

As the late Petr Skrabanek pointed out, human beings would have to drink approximately 24,000,000 cups of decaffeinated coffee to receive a dose of the alleged carcinogenic chemicals equivalent to that received by those unfortunate laboratory mice. It is clear that 24,000,000 cups of any liquid whatsoever would exert unhappy effects upon the human frame. Skrabanek calculated that to decide whether the tiny doses of chemicals remaining in decaffeinated coffee are carcinogenic in mice at equivalent doses would probably require an experiment on 8,000,000,000 laboratory mice – assuming what is almost certainly not true, that the relationship between dose and carcinogenicity is a linear one.

Even this extensive experiment might not determine whether the chemicals used in the decaffeination of coffee were carcinogenic in Man, however. For it is notoriously the case that what is carcinogenic in one species of mammal is not necessarily carcinogenic in another. What is safe for mice is not safe for humans, and vice versa. However safe a substance proves to be in tests upon animals, a doubt must remain about its safety in humans. If the bacillus which causes leprosy had been (shall we say) a new drug developed by a pharmaceutical company, it would have appeared perfectly safe in tests upon the commonly used laboratory animals, for it is pathogenic in none of them. (For many years, *Mycobacterium leprae* – a close relative of the tubercle bacillus – could not be transmitted to any living organism except Man. Then, after a search lasting nearly a century, it was discovered that it would grow in the foot-pad of the armadillo. It is most unlikely that any pharmaceutical company would have researched its product on so *recherché* a tissue; nor could it possibly have been held negligent for not having done so.) Moreover, given the slow pace of the development of leprosy as a disease, the fact that the pharmaceutical company's hypothetically safe product was in fact causing serious disease would not have been appreciated until it was too late.

Undue extrapolation from toxicology, and a constant eye to its latest (but provisional) findings, can poison minds more effectively than the vast majority of proposed toxins poison bodies. Undigested science can simultaneously both cause undue alarm and lull into a false sense of security, implying as it may do to those unfamiliar with the ways of science that everything is already known. When this turns out to be an illusion – when, for example, a new drug turns out to have unanticipated deleterious side-effects – anger often results, soon to be followed by the search for a scape-goat and, naturally enough, for compensation. The fact that pharmacutical companies have sometimes either been careless in their premature marketing of a drug, or have actively sought to suppress inconvenient scientific informa-tion about it, lends an *a priori* justification to this anger, even when in fact it is not justified. The underlying assumption of most people is that if all the rules are scrupulously obeyed, then nothing can go wrong and safety will be assured.

The case of decaffeinated coffee is by no means the sole example of a health scare caused by the mistaken, and intrinsically implausible, extrapolation of experimental toxicology to the everyday life of Man. There are numerous such examples. Among the most striking of this genre was the case of alar, a substance sprayed on apples to retard their deterioration which was denounced in 1986 as carcinogenic by consumer protection groups in the United States (which, of course, never recognise that they have any vested interests of their own to protect – vested inter-ests being by definition interests which belong to someone else. One's own interests are never vested.) It was demon-strated that if children came into contact with the kind of quantities of apple juice in which they were more likely to drown than to drink, that is to say 24,000 cartons per day, they might develop cancer – that is, if they were mice.

Despite the intrinsic implausibility of the evidence and the unfounded nature of the premises upon which the allegations were made, the American public reacted much as it had when Orson Welles dramatised H. G. Wells's *War of the Worlds* on the radio and announced that the Martians were landing: with panic. It was believed at once that an apple a day kept the oncologist in pay. Sales of apple juice plummeted, farmers faced ruin, and apples were shunned as if they were the cast-off clothing of people who had died during the Black Death. In fact, it would probably be possible to demonstrate that more apple farmers died of suicide because of the alar scare than consumers of apples ever died from the effects of alar itself.

Publicity given to very rare events may also serve to raise anxieties – or awareness, in the mealy-mouthed expression of the health educationists. For example, it has been known for people who are allergic to seafood such as prawns to have a reaction to the vapour of seafood given off as it passes them on sizzling hotplates in restaurants, and there is even one recorded case of resultant death. In response to this surpassingly rare event, Canadian restaurateurs have been encouraged to inform themselves about food allergies, so that they can inform their worried customers about the dangers hidden in their dishes, to learn about resuscitation and to provide areas of their restaurants which are guaranteed free of sizzling hotplates. Henceforth every meal in a Canadian restaurant is to be considered a potential last supper.

Some people claim nowadays to be allergic to practically everything (except, happily, those few things which are necessary for the continuation of life itself). They ascribe this curious omnihypersensitivity to the presence in the world of so many unnatural and industrially produced chemicals, which play havoc with their delicate 'systems'. They sometimes describe themselves as allergic to the twentieth century: it is the modern equivalent of Cheyne's 'English Malady', that vapourishness which was supposed to indicate a superior (and of course suffering) soul.

One can sympathise with anybody who finds certain aspects of our century unattractive; but those who suffer from total allergy syndrome and must live in remote parts of the countryside (though connected to the electricity supply and the telephone network) to avoid as many of the noxious chemicals as possible should count themselves lucky that they were not living in the nineteenth century, when doctors might well have dosed them with compounds containing antimony, mercury or arsenic (the last for indigestion).

XV

As every child knows who has ever read a fairy story, there is something not altogether displeasing about fright. The big dipper in amusement parks depends upon the pleasures of terror as completely as restaurants depend upon the pleasures of the table. In adolescence, I adored the Dracula films which were then in vogue and frequently made me jump out of my skin. Even at that early age, however, I was able to leave my terror behind me in the cinema, for I had already learnt to distinguish between the real and the imaginary; and though on my way home I passed an unilluminated graveyard of ancient establishment, I did not expect to be pursued by revenants of any description.

Many people actively seek danger, and some are never happier than when clambering up a sheer cliff face, on which the slightest error of judgement or miscalculation – to say nothing of the eternal possibility of ill luck – must mean a swift death. It is impossible to believe that these climbers are unaware at any moment of the danger they are in, for this danger is one of the attractions of an otherwise pointless activity. Nor do I believe that this love of danger is simply a desire for, or addiction to, rushes of adrenaline, as some have suggested. The matter lies far deeper than that.

I have met journalists for whom anything less than full civil war is tedious to report or to live through, and have myself experienced the heightened awareness of existence and the value of life in situations of chronic danger and uncertainty such as civil war. Never does one feel more alive, in fact, than at moments when one is thrown entirely on one's own resources to extricate oneself from danger, during periods when every tree, every hill and every home could conceal the means of one's imminent destruction. The return thereafter to a more settled and safer existence is not always easy; for by comparison with an existence in which every act or omission is potentially a matter of life and death, mere safety must seem a tame kind of virtue, and the daily concerns of life in modern industrial democracies seem bland, banal and trivial. Even in Switzerland they feel obliged to riot now and again, just to assure themselves that they are still alive and capable of feeling emotions about something.

No doubt the taste for danger can be explained in

evolutionary terms: when Man came of age in the savan-
nahs of East Africa, big bad animals abounded, and he had
better have had his wits about him.* If fright were going to
make him unhappy, early Man would have been miserable
indeed, and suicide would have been preferable to the
continuation of life which, *a priori*, would have endangered
the species or the genes which it carried. Therefore a cheerful disposition in the face of danger, or an actual taste for
it, would have been of survival value. Man is made for
peace and tranquillity as crocodiles are made for a vegetarian diet.

So it is not altogether surprising that we all enjoy a good
scare now and again, especially now that life is virtually
free of genuine or immanent risk. We have to invent risks
to persuade ourselves that, appearances to the contrary
notwithstanding, we – or those we love – are actually in as
much danger as ever. That is the real reason why we dress
up our children in bicycle helmets, though the chances
that such helmets will have any effect other than the
promotion of anxiety neurosis in their wearers are slender
(and neurotics of all kinds, be it remembered, have a
higher death rate than those few of us not afflicted with
neurosis). It will surely not be long, once all bicyclists are
safely helmeted, before someone will propose that pedestrians follow suit by wearing helmets also (and gardeners,

---

* Sociobiology, which explains Man's conduct by reference to his evolutionary past and biological constitution, looks set fair at the end of our
century to take over where Freudianism and Marxism left off, or were
forced to leave off, in their explanation of Man's behaviour: explanations
which denied the role of conscious thought as a vital determinant of
Man's fate, at least in civilised society. Instead of being the plaything of
his upbringing, or of his place in the division of labour, Man under sociobiology becomes – not for the first time, and probably not for the last –
the plaything of his genes.

inasmuch as I read in the newspaper yesterday that a
woman was killed by a falling branch in her garden).

The great advantage of frightening ourselves with risks
which, if they exist at all, are so slight as to be scarcely
measurable, is that we get all the existential kudos of living
in danger without having our lives imperilled in any way
whatsoever. In a world full of dangers, nothing is without
significance. Indeed, we must all be brave indeed to carry
on with our daily lives in the face of so many unseen yet
acknowledged hazards. The word *survivor*, which was once
used of people who emerged alive from shipwrecks or
concentration camps in which many others died, is now
used of anyone who continues to live after any unpleasant
experience, even those which pose no conceivable threat to
life.

It may seem at first sight contradictory that while on the
one hand we regard every death as exceptional, unnatural
and wholly avoidable, on the other we conceive of the
world as filled with the myriad death-dealing slings and
arrows of outrageous fortune. But mere contradiction does
not, in practice, prevent us from thinking anything at all:
logical incompatibility does not prevent us from resolutely
maintaining two directly opposite propositions about the
same subject simultaneously. Besides which the contradiction is more apparent than real, inasmuch as a world full
of dangers allows us at the same time to explain the anomaly of death, to hope for immortality once all dangers are
identified and removed, and to feel delightfully aggrieved
that our deaths are the consequence of the unbridled freedom granted to vested interests.

Several factors do conspire, in fact, to maintain us in a
state of permanent panic over trifles. (I don't, of course,
mean that there is an actual conspiracy, with all the

administrative structure, such as secret meetings, that a real conspiracy entails.)

First we must be kept in a condition receptive to the consumption of new goods and services which allegedly promote our health. For example, health check-ups were advocated long before there was evidence that they were of any value whatever in the preservation of life or limb (there still isn't any). It has been estimated – though personally I mistrust such estimates – that fully one-eighth of the American economy is devoted to health care, and if present trends continue a time will come when looking after each other's health will be the sole economic activity. It is clear that if people were now to take their health for granted, and to stop worrying about it, there might well be a sudden contraction in economic activity such as would dwarf that produced by the crash of 1929. Seen in macroeconomic terms, therefore, mass hypochondriasis is a Keynesian mechanism for maintaining aggregate demand. An increase in the level of hypochondriasis acts like an increase in government expenditure during a recession. Remember, then, that when you fret over a twinge you feel in your abdomen or elsewhere in your body, you are engaged in the great humanitarian enterprise of keeping vast numbers of people employed who otherwise might have difficulty in finding employment.

Second, there is now more than one bureaucracy – some of them self-constituted and self-appointed – which depend for their continued existence upon an atmosphere of disquiet and alarm. This is not to say that *none* of their work is legitimate or valuable. For example, the system which in Britain surveys the side-effects of medicaments, particularly while they are still new and relatively untried, performs a signal service. But it is not a service which will ever exert more than a marginal effect on the heath of the population; and in general the advantages of vigilance can be overbalanced by the unjustified anxiety to which it gives rise. It is one thing for our water to be free of bacteria, and for our dairy products to be pasteurised; it is quite another to treat every supermarket as if it were managed by Lucrezia Borgia.

The demand for information about the ingredients of the food we buy, for example, which emanates from consumer pressure groups, is generally regarded as justified and enlightened: do we not have the right to know what we are eating, so that we may make an informed choice? Unfortunately, such information can be both dishonest and profoundly trivialising of life itself. It may be dishonest because it is impossible to give a full chemical analysis of any food and because, even if it were possible, the effects on human health of most of the ingredients would be either unknown or controversial and equivocal, and even if they were known in full they would have to be compared with alternatives for anyone to come to what is known as a fully informed and rational decision about what to buy. If everything is harmful to some extent, in some circumstances, in some quantities or some combinations (even water can cause intoxication and even death when consumed to excess), it is not enough to know the contents and properties of any given food one is thinking of buying: one must know the contents and properties of all the rest. One cannot, after all, choose between medicines solely on the basis of their side-effects.

The demands for information are dishonest because they systematically deny the complexities and ambiguity of the scientific evidence; and because they do not recognise that, since knowledge is incomplete and will for ever remain incomplete, life cannot be lived as a series of informed choices. In a sense, every meal is a leap in the dark, as far as one's health is concerned; but fortunately it is a leap over a vanishingly tiny empty space, since there is every reason to believe that the content of one's diet – within a wide range of adequate diets – plays little part in one's health.

And the demands of consumer pressure groups for 'complete' information about the foods we buy are trivialising because they make the prolongation of life the main end of life itself. In their philosophy, the avoidance of mathematical risk is the highest good; and they would like to make every purchase of food, every mouthful of food, the outcome of an agonised and detailed calculation which it would take a supercomputer to make, the practical difference between the various decisions – to buy or not to buy, to eat or not to eat – being of submicroscopic dimensions.

To agonise over trifles is not merely foolish, it is self-indulgent and wicked. It is an expense of spirit in a waste of shame.

XVI

The chief purpose of the dissemination of health statistics has become the fostering of political discontent and the promotion of anxiety. When such anxiety becomes chronic, there is only one solution: to collect more statistics and subject them to even closer scrutiny.

One of the chief handmaidens of panic is the concept of

relative risk. If you can demonstrate that the consumer of x is 2.3 times more likely develop y, where x is an item of common or universal consumption and y is a disease, preferably fatal or at least horrible, you have an incipient panic on your hands. It does not matter in the least that the disease is so rare that, even at 2.3 times its 'normal' incidence, most doctors would never see a case if they had ten careers instead of one. What is important, from the point of view of raising anxiety, is that there should be an increase.

Passive smoking is said to raise the risk of contracting lung cancer. Those non-smokers whose spouses smoke are said to have a rate of lung cancer 1.5 times that of non-smokers whose spouses are also non-smokers. An increase of 50 per cent sounds a lot, and so it would be if, for example, one were talking of an event which were quite likely to happen in any case, such as a heart attack. But lung cancer (of the kind caused by smoking) is so rare in non-smokers that research on the subject has been difficult to conduct and the results controversial. The original research was flawed, some repeat studies failed to show the alleged effect, and scientific agreement has not been reached. The effect, if it exists at all, must be a small one.

This has not in the least detained enthusiasts, whose thirst for action is greater perhaps than their love of statistical minutiae.* After all, it is inconceivable that second-hand or lung cigarette smoke does anyone any good; we no longer believe, as our forefathers did, that smoking protects

---

* I have no particular axe to grind in this matter. I do not own shares in any tobacco company, nor have I received any payment from one, as is often alleged against those who express even minimal reservations about one or other aspect of the campaign against smoking – as if owning shares or receiving subventions were the only possible form of corrupting vested interest which might affect a man's judgement. Personally, I dislike smoking intensely, though for purely aesthetic reasons.

against the plague, or that cigarette smoke may be good for asthma, as one leading British textbook of medicine alleged as late as 1942, only a decade before Sir Richard Doll established its link with lung cancer in the eyes of the world (the researches of the Nazi doctors, for obvious reasons, had failed to persuade anyone). And if there were only a single death in the whole history of the world attributable to passive smoking, that unnecessary death would in itself be sufficient to justify the sternest measures to protect the innocent against the potential harm of passive smoking. Indeed, so dire is the threat now considered that adoption authorities have tried to forbid the adoption of children by smokers. The justification for their high-handedness is that the children of parents who smoke are more liable than the children of non-smokers to develop bronchitis and asthma; and their resolve will be made all the more adamantine by the publication of studies demonstrating that the babies of smokers are more susceptible to cot death, of which there are about a hundred a year in the entire country, and to which the smoking of adoptive parents must make a minimal contribution. It surely cannot be too long before smoking in the presence of children is defined as a type of child abuse: this in a country in which the gross neglect of children is scandalously routine and implicitly accepted.

But what if one were the single person to die as the result of passive inhalation of other people's cigarette smoke? When you consider how important your own life is to you and to those who love you, and how unimportant it is that anyone should smoke, for smoking is at best a trivial pleasure, then a certain justified anger wells up in you, and you raise your voice against this terrible but avoidable carnage. At least then you will not have died in vain. The fact that you are most unlikely to die in this fashion in the first place will not inhibit you: for passions are more easily stirred by phantoms than by realities, besides which they are more fun to combat.

Just in case anyone should fail to get the message, and ask not for the relative but the absolute risk of contracting lung cancer from passive smoking, it is made extemely difficult for him to find it – because, of course, the risk is so small that it is not worth worrying about, let alone undertaking a stringent and repressive campaign to eliminate.

When the concept of relative risk might lead to complacency rather than to panic, on the other hand, it is not only abandoned at once, but is repudiated thoroughly. For a number of years, North America and Western Europe have been threatened with an epidemic of AIDS among the great majority of the population which does not fall into the main groups heretofore affected by the disease. The threat seems to have come more from the epidemiologists than from the epidemic itself, for the long-promised indiscriminate spread of the disease has resolutely failed to materialise. In fact, it has proved rather easy for the great bulk of the population to avoid AIDS: all it has had to do is refrain from injecting itself with needles shared with drug addicts, having anal intercourse without the protection of condoms, and promiscuous sexual intercourse with the inhabitants of Central Africa. This has not, on the whole, required much of a change in habits.

Has there been universal rejoicing at the good fortune of the majority, that in effect it has nothing much to worry about, at least with regard to catching AIDS? Not a bit of it. There has been a kind of *schadenfreude* in reverse; and suddenly those who might normally be expected to worry over trivial risks, such as those entailed by passive smoking, turn and attack the very idea of a group at risk as being inherently stigmatising and degrading to those who are so designated.

There are two main reasons for this curious reversal of attitudes. The first is that the two groups most afflicted with the disease in Europe and North America are minorities – homosexuals and drug addicts – and minorities must, at least if they have been despised, looked down upon and oppressed in the past, have their sensibilities soothed by circumlocution. Thus intellectuals, playing their accustomed game of more-compassionate-and-sensitive-than-thou, tie themselves up in semantic knots in their attempts to deny the obvious. It isn't drug addicts as a group of human beings who are at risk, it is the behaviour of sharing needles which is the problem: therefore it is wrong and dehumanising to label drug addicts as a risk group for AIDS. No one, of course, had ever objected before to this way of putting things: for example, to the stigmatising of alcoholics as a group peculiarly susceptible to cirrhosis of the liver; or claimed that it wasn't alcoholics as such who were a risk group, but rather the repeated raising of glasses filled with alcoholic drinks to the lips and the subsequent pouring of them down the throat which was the problem. It was as though describing homosexuals as a group at special risk of contracting AIDS was tantamount to an endorsement or even a provocation of the violence which is sometimes offered to homosexuals on the street, allegedly in retaliation for having brought this disease into the world, but in fact for the pure and undiluted pleasure of beating up the vulnerable and weak.*

* The treatment of homosexuals and people infected with the human immunodeficiency virus in Cuba has not been the object of as many or as vigorous denunciations as these policies might have evoked had they been carried out by another type of regime. Far from having been tainted with Original Sin, Castro appears to have been blessed with Original Virtue.

There was, in fact, outright official denial of the epidemiological predilections of the AIDS virus. In Britain, for example, there was a mass publicity campaign whose slogan was 'AIDS isn't prejudiced'. In the strict philosophical sense, of course, the slogan was correct: prejudices belong to minds, and neither a virus nor the syndrome it causes has a mind. But if the slogan meant to imply, as surely it did, that nobody was at greater risk than anybody else of becoming infected with the virus, it was not merely misleading, it was outright mendacious. It would hardly have been more dishonest to have run an advertising campaign – perhaps with the object of raising money for research – with the slogan 'Lung cancer isn't prejudiced'. The epidemiological justification would have been the same: some people with lung cancer have never smoked in their lives.

The second reason for this curious ambivalence towards the concept of a risk group is the thirst for power and for the right of interference in the lives of others on the part of those who believe themselves to have a providential role in the securing of the health of the population. It is acceptable to believe that children of smokers are at special risk of various illnesses because this belief provides a justification for officialdom to exercise arbitrary power; whereas it is unacceptable to believe that homosexuals are at special risk of AIDS because this belief severely limits the importance of an entire self-generated bureaucracy, and calls the need for its very existence into question.

When the concept of relative risk conduces to anxiety and panic, it is emphasised, but when on the contrary it might lead to complacency and relaxation, it is forgotten. One is reminded of the Cheshire cat, which disappeared, leaving only its grin behind; similarly, the details of epidemiology disappear, leaving only anxiety behind.

XVII

There have been so many health scares in the past twenty years that no one could possibly keep up with them or make a comprehensive list of them. The consumption of green potatoes during pregancy was once thought to cause neural tube defects in babies such as spina bifida;* twenty years later, the consumption of grapefruit juice at breakfast was publicised as interfering fatally with the metabolism of certain drugs.

---

* Such a theory might well have induced unnecessary and cruel guilt in mothers who gave birth to such babies. What did I do during my pregancy to cause this? There must surely have been something: one is reminded of the ancient theory, firmly subscribed to through most of human history, that a mother affrighted during a pregnancy by an unusual sight would give birth to a baby which in one respect or another would reflect not merely the fact that the mother had been frightened, but the actual cause of that fright. Thus the Elephant Man's mother was startled during pregancy by the then highly exotic sight of an elephant.

Extensive publicity given to equally mistaken hypotheses, couched in the language of modern science and research, may not be entirely harmless, and may rapidly turn into superstition. The idea that schizophrenia was caused by disordered family relationships, and even the existence of the family as such, was once, during the 1960s, propagated with an evangelical zeal not proportional to the evidence in its favour, for reasons quite distinct from any sympathy with the sufferers from this condition (if indeed it is a unitary phenomenon). The problem with such theories is not only that they induce inappropriate guilt and add to the distress of the already distressed, but that they may distract from real and tangible risks to health which are already known to exist. The result is that people waste their efforts in trying to avoid the unavoidable, while accepting the avoidable with mulish indifference.

From listeria in soft cheese and pâtés causing miscarriages to salmonella in eggs causing fatal food poisoning, especially in the elderly; from hormones in the water supply – emanating from the recycled urine of women on the pill – causing a decline in the sperm count* to high-voltage wires causing leukaemia; from the endocrine effects of plastic wrappings to the carcinogenic effects of margarine; from bananas and orange juice causing violent crime (the solution to which is a change of diet) to genetically engineered new varieties of corn and soya bean being such a general threat to the world's health that Greenpeace activists felt compelled to occupy cranes in Liverpool docks: never a moment's rest, repose or peace of mind for today's busy hypochondriac. He may have forgotten the fright of all his yesterdays, but that never prevents him from being frightened by the latest epidemiological research, which, with a little bit of imagination and obsessionality, can be transmuted into anxiety and even terror.

The fact that disasters do sometimes happen nourishes this fear and expectation. Occasionally deadly toxins find their way into the food supply and wreak brief but all too real havoc. It is scarcely to be expected that scores of millions of people can be fed day after day, year after year, without a mishap ever occurring. But such accidents can hardly compare with, say, the routine contamination of the food supply in the Middle Ages, when rye bread impregnated with fungus caused epidemics of ergotism; or with the milk supply of late-eighteenth-century London:

* I repeat, the people who worry about the declining sperm count are the same people who – by temperament – worry about the overpopulation of the world.

Every Cow-house is provided with a milk-room (where the milk is measured and served out by the Cow-keeper) and the room is mostly furnished with *a pump*, to which the Retail Dealers apply in rotation; not secretly, but openly before any person that may be standing by, from which they pump water into the milk vessels at their discretion. The pump is placed there expressly for that purpose, and indeed is very seldom used for any other. A considerable Cow-keeper has a pump of this kind, which goes by the name of *Famous Black Cow* (from the circumstance of it being painted black), *and is said to yield more than all the rest put together*.

Where such a pump is not provided for them things are much worse, for in that case the Retailers are not even careful to use *clean* water. Some of them have been seen to dip their pails in a common horse-trough. And what is still more disgusting, though equally true, one cow-house happens to stand close to the edge of a stream, into which runs much of the dung, and most of the urine of the cows, and even in this stream, so foully impregnated, they have been observed to dip their milk-pails. . .

No person could possibly drink of the milk, were they fully acquainted with the filthy manners of these dealers in it.

The written description alone is sufficient to make one feel queasy; and while modern contamination of the food supply can be dramatic, it is usually circumscribed in time and extent. Minamata Disease, for example, was caused when surplus metallic mercury, which had been used as a catalyst in the manufacture of acetaldehyde, was released into the waters of Minamata Bay in Japan. The mercury was converted into methyl mercury by the sea plants in the water, and thereby entered the food chain. Hundreds of people were affected neurologically by the methyl mercury in the fish and shellfish which they ate, and the cause was not established for some years. A similar outbreak occurred in Iraq in 1971, when 6,000 people were hospitalised (of whom 500 died) after eating bread made from wheat which had been dressed with methyl mercury as a fungicide. Contaminated cooking oil in the 1980s caused scores of deaths in Spain, and the supposed cause took many years to elucidate. But it is the very infrequency of these disasters which makes them so noteworthy: we have come to expect a perfectly safe food supply, and to an astonishing extent – at least by comparison with all previous eras in history – this has been achieved.

Drugs are sometimes marketed which turn out to have such serious side-effects that any beneficial effects or advantages over other drugs which they may have are trivial by comparison. Thalidomide is the best-known example (though it is still sometimes used in leprosy); a beta-blocker, practolol, caused a form of blindness; the anti-inflammatory drug benoxaprofen caused serious liver and skin disorders, and it was alleged that the pharmaceutical company which manufactured it was not wholly unaware of its dangerousness when it marketed it.

It is thus theoretically possible that any given health scare is justified, and that while it is easy in retrospect to see that it was not, and why it was not, life has to be lived forwards, not backwards. Wisdom after the event is by far the easiest kind of wisdom to attain, and by far the least useful.

But health scares which turn out to have been justified or reasonable, rather than having been based on illegitimate extrapolation of uncertain and unconfirmed scientific findings, are like air crashes: they happen, but rarely. A would-be traveller who cowered in the corner and refused to move because he knew that cars, buses, trains and aircraft sometimes crash, and ships sometimes sink, would be an object of pity; as should be the hypochondriac and health fanatic who eschews the ordinary pleasures of life because he fears they might harm him.

Perhaps the greatest health scare of the moment – at least as I write this, though it may have been supplanted by another by the time what I write reaches the presses – is that relating to the transmission of Creutzfeld-Jakob disease (CJD) to humans from cattle which suffer from Bovine Spongiform Encephalopathy (BSE). The scientific evidence is not yet decisive. But even if it should turn out that BSE had nothing whatever to do with feeding cattle with the rendered remains of sheep infected with scrapie, many people will still feel that this involuntary carnivorising of cattle, to boost the profits of farmers, was in such profound contradiction to Nature's intentions for cattle (themselves the result of human intervention, of course) that retribution in the form of sickness was deserved even if it was not actually produced. It is curious how those who would strenuously object to the idea that AIDS was in some sense the product of concupiscent or degraded behaviour are all too ready to condemn the unnatural practices of dairy farmers, in retribution for which the development of CJD was the inevitable result. It is as if the love of money is the only sin which modern Man is prepared to acknowledge and Nature likely to punish, all other sins – including the most insensate promiscuity and the lazy desire for an effortless entry into paradise evinced by drug takers – being downgraded to mere error at worst. Actually, Nature is indifferent to the sins and virtues of Man, from which very fact stems his moral responsibility; and the hatred of greed and the desire for gain which so many intellectuals express (in words if not in deeds) partake of the quality of envy, itself a sin of some magnitude and width of distribution.

Whatever the scientific truth about BSE and CJD turns out to be, two rather curious features about the ensuing panic struck me immediately. The first was the glee with which the direst predictions were made, and the second was the pattern of European abstinence from beef which was provoked by the scare.

In the past two weeks I have read of at least three threats to the continuation of the human race, without in the least searching for them, and all propounded more or less seriously: a rogue asteroid, mutant viruses and intelligent man-made machines whose intelligence would render humanity redundant (in *El Heraldo* of Cartagena; *Virus X* by Frank G. Ryan, Collins, 1996; and the *Sunday Telegraph* of 15 December 1996, respectively). Am I to conclude that the human race really is in danger on several fronts at once, or that for some reason people find the prospect of total annihilation exciting and, in a strange way, comforting? Perhaps deep inside they know that, technological miracles notwithstanding, they are going one day to die, and therefore – since they believe in no transcendent purpose or meaning to life – universal death is a consolation to them. At least they will not die alone; and like the jealous but jilted murderer who says of his lover, 'If I can't have her, no one else will', they say, 'At least if I am dead, so will everyone else be.' Thenceforth there will be no waking on a summer's morning, no dinner parties, no matinée theatre performances, no pleasure of any kind, in short no continuation of life after my death just as if nothing of supreme importance had happened: the rest will well and truly be silence. If I cannot continue to live, why should anyone else?

In this connection, the Paraguayan dictator Francisco Solano Lopez expired with the words, 'I die with my country!' on his lips, though it might just as well have been the other way round, 'My country dies with me!' By the time of his death in 1870, nineteen out of twenty male Paraguayans had died or been killed in the War of the Triple Alliance – Argentina, Brazil and Uruguay – which Lopez had himself provoked and continued out of vanity, as pointless a conflict as any in history. And who would be prepared to say for certain that Saddam Hussein would not prefer the extinction of his country to its continuation without him? It is instructive to compare the attitude of these *Götterdämmerung* dictators (whose egotism is only that of Everyman writ large) with that of the fictional king in Ionesco's *Le Roi se meurt*, when he is told that he is dying:

Without me, without me. They'll laugh, they'll picnic, they'll dance on my grave. It'll be as if I had never existed. Ah, let them remember me. Let them cry, let them despair. Let them perpetuate my memory in all the history books. Let everyone know my life by heart. Let everyone relive it. Let schoolchildren and scholars have no other subject than me, my kingdom, my deeds. Let them burn all other books, let them destroy all other statues, let them put mine in all the public squares. My picture in all the ministries, in all the police stations, in all the tax offices, in all the hospitals. Let them name all aircraft, all ships, all vehicles after me. Let all the other kings, soldiers, poets, tenors, philosophers be forgotten and let all thoughts be about me. Only one first name, only one surname for everybody. Let them learn to read by spelling my name . . . Let me be on all the icons, let me be on all the millions of crosses in the churches. Let them say masses for me, let me be the Host. Let all windows be the colour and shape of my eyes, let all rivers draw the profile of my face on the plains! Let them call upon me, let them beg me, let them implore me, for ever and ever.

The existential emptiness behind this speech is the same that finds the prospect of the end of humanity – or at least a large portion of it – reassuring.

So it was not altogether surprising – when a possible connection between BSE and CJD was first mooted, and ten deaths were publicised from a new kind of CJD among young people not normally considered at risk, but who had probably eaten a lot of hamburgers, and the possibility that there was such a link was finally admitted by officialdom which until then had denied it – that experts came forward to opine that more than ten million people in the British Isles alone might have been infected and would in due course die of the disease. It was just what we wanted to hear, it brightened up our day no end, though some foreigners might find it rather difficult to distinguish between a British population with and without a sixth of its population prematurely demented.

Whenever a disaster has occurred anywhere in the world, I make it a rule to divide the number of victims by a factor of at least four, or, if the disaster is in a country not usually mentioned in the news at all, by a factor of ten: extra exaggeration having been necessary to secure publication in the first place. Division by a factor of a hundred, a thousand or even ten thousand is necessary when estimating realistically the effects of disasters still to come, and which are anticipated with sanguinary eagerness. Such disasters are always the worst ever, of course, and quite unprecedented. In an age when newspapers routinely devote more space to what *might* happen than to what *has* happened, health disasters still to materialise are definitely the most serviceable and the most sought after. A disease which might, at its apogee, eventually affect a hundred or a thousand people is of no more use as a news story than a house that hasn't been burgled.

It was also only to be expected that sales of beef would fall in those countries in which there was some possibility of developing the disease, at least if the theory of its causation were true. But when the decline in the sales of beef is compared for Britain, France and Germany, what do we find? If the theory of causation were true, the people of Britain would be most at risk, the French next and the Germans least – because of the pattern of British beef exports. The fall in the sales of beef was in the opposite order, however: the greatest in Germany and the least in Britain. The Germans, apparently, were reluctant to eat beef which was unlikely ever to have been infected. In short, they reacted like those tourists who cancel holidays in Greece because a bomb has gone off in Cairo.

XVIII

When mice and other small animals are threatened by danger which is beyond their capacity to resist or avoid, they sit stock-still and wash their paws, as if dirty paws were the problem. No doubt there is some deep evolutionary wisdom in this seemingly irrational and pointless conduct: not every overwhelming danger turns out to be fatal, after all, and rhythmical activity no doubt calms the frazzled nerves of terrified mice.

Man is no different; but his displacement activities (as they are called) take place with a patina of intellectual justification, as befits the vast expansion of his cerebral hemispheres.

We fear what is not likely to happen, the better to avoid thinking about what is. In part, this is because the unusual grips our imagination as the quotidian does not; moreover, it does not matter how many times we tell ourselves that statistics conclusively prove that air travel is the safest method of conveyance from one place to another, there must be very few of us who, when an aircraft in which we are travelling takes off or is about to land, do not experience the faintest glimmer of apprehension. That such vast machines should take off and land without mishap seems wildly improbable to the untutored mind; in vain, therefore, do we try to expunge from our imaginations the pictures of twisted and smoking wreckage we sometimes see on television after an airliner has plunged to earth or crashed into a mountainside soon after take-off. No matter what the statistics say about the relative safety of travel by air and bus, Catholics do not cross themselves on departure from the bus station, nor do Italians applaud when a bus reaches its destination; though if crossing oneself were truly a protection against disaster, it would more profitably be done on the bus than the aircraft.

With so many risks adumbrated each week – today gases from mattresses cause cot deaths, tomorrow smoking causes sperm damage leading to an increased likelihood of childhood cancers – it is hardly to be wondered at that people are no longer very good at distinguishing between the seriousness of risks. A risk a day keeps common sense away. For if risk lies everywhere, some people conclude that it hardly matters what they do, when their number's up their number's up – so they might as well continue smoking, despite the clear and unequivocal evidence of its dangers.

Often it is ill-appreciated that a small increase in a high risk can be more significant, from the point of view of lives lost, than a large increase in a low risk. A 1 per cent increase in deaths from a disease which causes a hundred thousand deaths a year results in more than twice as many extra deaths as a thousand per cent increase in deaths from a disease which causes fifty deaths a year. But fluctuations in the death rate from heart attack (still by far the most common cause of death in the Western world) do not generally attract our attention – especially as the trend is downwards. But would even a 1 per cent increase in the rate of fatal heart attack, which would mean 1,250 deaths in a year in Britain, attract anything like the headlines of the fifteen deaths so far from the new variant of Creutzfeld-Jakob disease? It was ever thus: in the nineteenth century, epidemics of cholera, then a new disease, attracted far more attention than tuberculosis, which actually killed far more people, but which seemed part of everyday life as cholera did not.

The raw numbers of people dying of a disease are not the only numbers which count, of course. Stroke may kill many times the number of people who die in road accidents, but when presented as the number of years of life lost, the order is decisively reversed. This is because people who die of strokes tend to be of advanced years in any case, with relatively few years to live even if they had not had a stroke; whereas the fatal victims of road accidents tend to be young. Let us suppose that the average life expectancy is seventy-five years, and that Disease A kills 100 children aged five, while Disease B kills 5,000 adults at the age of seventy-four. Which is more serious from the public health point of view?

Disease B kills fifty times as many people as Disease A, therefore it is fifty times as important. Disease A, on the other hand, is responsible for the loss of 7,000 years of life, while Disease B is responsible for the loss of only 5,000. Therefore Disease A is 1.4 times as important as Disease B.

Is there any value-free way of assigning relative importance to these two diseases? No: two reasonable people might disagree, without either being provably in the wrong. A man might say that young life is intrinsically more valuable than old, but there is no evidence which compels him to do so. The death of a baby – who has no fixed intentions or projects to accomplish – is not more tragic than that of a middle-aged man with much he still wants to do, merely because the baby still had more years to live.

Given, then, the complexities of 'objective' risk assessment, and the difficulties inherent in deciding between the costs and desirability of various outcomes, the ease with which people may be scared by the publicity given to slight increases in negligible risks and thereby panicked into unnecessary avoidance behaviour is not astonishing.* The problem arises because they are worrying, and worrying constantly, over risks to their health. And the central paradox is that the more people are justified in assuming that they will live to a ripe old age, the more hypochondriacal and worried they become. Their metaphysical condition approaches that of the princess of the fairy story who is able to prove that she and not another is the real princess because she is unable to sleep with a single pea under a hundred mattresses.

But why should modern Man be running scared when he has a better chance than ever before of seeing the sun rise tomorrow and the day after and the day after that? The answer, I think, is in his condition of existential funk. In his heart of hearts he knows that, whatever the technological miracles performed and yet to be performed, he is still as tied as ever he was to mortality. And he knows also that it is not a mortality which leads to anything: life is not an antechamber to a felicitous and never-ending existence on some other plane. On the contrary, modern Man knows that life is a brief interval of consciousness between two

---

* I once had a patient who was diabetic and much overweight. He told me quite frankly that smoking, drinking and eating rich food were so important to him that he would rather continue and die young than live abstemiously to a ripe old age. He did not deny the risks: he accepted them. I respected his decision, and even admired it, though I doubt I should have had the courage to emulate him if I had found myself in his condition. He did die young, but he had undoubtedly enjoyed his life to the full.

eternities of oblivion. And while there are those who argue
– not usually on their deathbed – that, since we do not fear
the aeons of non-being which preceded our birth, there is no
reason why we should fear similar aeons of non-being after
our death, fear of death remains almost universal: for us,
our birth and coming into consciousness are events of cardi-
nal and absolute importance, which decisively changed,
indeed created, the universe. Moreover, though the
Copernican and Darwinian revolutions may have demoted
Man's place in the natural world somewhat in the intellectual sphere, in the psychological and moral sphere his
importance as an individual has been growing exponentially, in so far as the doctrine of intrinsic rights is accepted
by everyone and extended to ever more aspects of existence.

As science pushes back the frontier of the unknown and
even the unknowable, the realm of mystery contracts.
There is now, as a friend of mine's daughter put it, a widespread *fear of the known*: a fear which arises as it becomes
ever clearer that there is nothing to life other than life itself.

Our brief interlude of consciousness being all we have,
therefore, an extra year or two of it (or come the time, an
extra half-hour of it), though insignificant from the statistical point of view, is everything and all-important. We are
not frightened of the electromagnetic radiation which
emanates from high-tension electric cables above us because
of the increase in the rate of leukaemia it allegedly brings
about in those who live near or under such cables, but
because we are scared *tout court*. Adapting slightly Emilia's
dictum in *Othello* about jealousy, we might say that:

> The anxious are not ever anxious for the cause,
> But they are anxious that they are anxious.

The desire to hang on to life is the root of all health scares.

It might be objected, of course, that the country in the Western world which is the *fons et origo* of the whole health-scare movement, if one can call it such, is the United States, which is also the Western country with by far the highest proportion of religious believers. Survey after survey demonstrates that the Americans have not lost their faith in God, or at least answer 'Yes' to questions posed in surveys about His existence. If health scares are themselves a symptom of existential funk, surely the Americans, secure in their belief in a transcendent being who serves as the guarantor that life has a purpose, should not be prey to them?

But an affirmative answer to a simple question in a survey or a questionnaire is hardly proof of the kind of faith which might protect someone from the kind of fundamental fear I have in mind. Such faith is probably not universal at the best of times, and these are not the best of times for faith: as Karl Popper pointed out, even to attempt a proof of God's existence is halfway to atheism, inasmuch as it implies the possibility of his non-existence. The man who demands proof has already lost his wholehearted belief; and the kind of believer for whom death has no fears is the kind of believer whose faith is so strongly and unselfconsciously held, and so deeply woven into the fabric of his existence, that there is no distinction between the sacred and profane.*

* I once heard of a Catholic nun, well into her nineties, who was expected to die in hospital overnight, an expectation which she fully shared. She not only survived the night, however, but woke refreshed; from which she concluded, despite the presence of a National Health Service breakfast nearby, that she had ascended to heaven. It took some time and effort – so the story went – to persuade her otherwise, and that the nurses were only metaphorical and not literal angels; but of the strength and psychologically protective power of her religious faith there could be no doubt in anyone's mind.

American religion is hardly of this intensity. It is true that members of fanatical American sects sometimes startle the world by committing mass suicide, evidence alike of the psychopathic nature of their leaders and the high price of gullibility; but in the main, an American's belief in God does not intrude very onerously into the day-to-day business of life. It would be difficult or impossible, indeed, for an observer on any given Wednesday or Thursday to detect much of a difference in the conduct of a believing and an unbelieving American.

The death of Philip II, to which I return, illustrates the kind of religious belief which, for good or ill, provides a man with that level of existential security which allows him to face death with true and unforced equanimity. Philip's death, as we have seen, was painful, lingering and slow. In life he had been meticulous about cleanliness, and was deeply (and unusually for the time) sensitive to bad smells and offensive sights; his last illness might have been designed by a malign enemy to make him suffer to the utmost. By all accounts, however, he bore it with immense fortitude, never uttering a complaint and remaining polite and considerate to his servants. His suffering never destroyed his faith in a benevolent God: for him, even the terrible dissolution of his body had meaning and purpose, and was part of the working out of a benign if somewhat undecipherable plan. Philip's apologists took his serenity as evidence of his saintliness, while his detractors took it as evidence of his unrepentant hardness of heart after all his many crimes. No one, however, denied that he died as all the witnesses testified: convinced that he was destined after his death for heaven.

The unflattering English view was that 'it is remarkable that he has arrived at that State of hypocritical

Insensibility and Delusion, that he thought all his Barbarities, Treachery, and Treasons were doing God's Service, and that he himself was ready to depart this Life in the Favour of God.' Spain was then the Enemy, of course, and it was impossible to believe anything good of a Spaniard; but even his most inveterate enemies did not doubt what it was that Philip believed.

At three in the morning of 13 September 1598, a few hours before his death, Philip was offered the crucifix which had belonged to his father, Charles V, who had decreed that it should be offered to his son at his hour of death. 'Give it to me,' said Philip, 'for the hour has come'; and he laughed. Fray José de Siguenza, who was present, interpreted Philip's laugh in the following way: 'For those fortunate souls that used the things of this world, and carried out their duties and enjoyed their earthly dignities with no real attachment, this is the moment when their true happiness begins, and they can laugh.' This seems to me to be entirely plausible in Philip's case. His apartments in the Escorial, where he died, are small and, while no doubt they were comfortable by the standards of the peasantry, they indicate no attachment to grandeur. His last act, when he woke briefly and for the final time from the stupor into which he had sunk, was to smother the crucifix with kisses.

I am not, of course, asserting that Philip's beliefs comforted him because they were true (on the contrary, I have no religious belief at all); nor am I asserting that his beliefs were in all respects socially and personally useful. These beliefs comforted Philip not only because he believed them to be true but because he was psychologically incapable of considering whether they might not be true.

Whatever else may be said of American suburban religion (and, by extension, most non-fringe religion in the Western world), it is not of this degree of personal intensity, and therefore fails to provide its adherents with the kind of consolation with which his intransigent and uncompromising Catholicism provided Philip. On the contrary – and in my personal experience of nominally religious people who are close to death – the modern believer might as well be an atheist for all the comfort his religion brings to him in the face of encroaching oblivion. Indeed, if the modern believer anticipates death with equanimity, it is not because he looks forward to meeting his maker and to heavenly reward, but because he believes the suffering he has endured in life is beyond relief and nothingness is preferable.

Naturally, there have been some non-believers who have faced death calmly in the absence of horrible suffering. The philosopher David Hume, whose nominal deism was surely only a fig-leaf for his fundamental but at that time unpublishable atheism, died a death which was by all accounts one of complete philosophical, indeed ironical, detachment. But Hume enjoyed certain advantages not enjoyed by most unbelievers: he had a naturally phlegmatic temperament, he had devoted his life to philosophical enquiry, and he left behind him a body of work which he must have known would keep his name and his memory alive as long as philosophy continued to interest men. Dead he might be about to be, but forgotten never.

The vast majority of us who do not believe – or who do not believe viscerally – in a divine or transcendent purpose in life have no such consolation in our last days as Hume's. Our lives are lived in a more or less perpetual state of disgruntlement and disappointed expectations, and the tasks to which we devote ourselves – paying the

mortgage, climbing the career ladder – are not such as
can offer us much hope that we shall be remembered
other than by those close to us for much more than a
month after we are gone. The ease with which the organisations in which we work continue to function the day
after the disappearance (by death, resignation or
dismissal) of someone who has devoted all his energies to
them hardly reassures us about our own deeper significance in the scheme of things. We know that we shall
disappear like a stone cast in a pond.

We do not even have any longer the consolation of the
ceremonies of death which consoled our forefathers (we
are too busy), and which continue to console those who
live in cultures where death is not an embarrassment, like
a *faux pas* at a diplomatic reception. For example, in the
little town of Mompox, in Colombia, the cemetery is obviously regarded as important in the life of the town, and
is meticulously cared for: not only are the tombs cleaned
and decorated every All Souls' Day, when the entire
population spends the day there, but on Sundays many
widows, widowers and children light candles and pray at
the graves of the departed. The bereaved talk unselfconsciously to the dead, as if they were still present; and thus
a dying man, knowing that he too will be talked to in this
fashion, has the consolation that he will not be forgotten
the moment the breath is out of him. The immediate
press of daily business will not engulf his memory as if he
had never been. And though he can hardly be expected to
be remembered once those who knew him have themselves passed away (to use the term which I hear in my
hospital every day, as though the avoidance of the use of
the verb *to die* will somehow propitiate death itself), the
future period in which no one is alive who knew him is so

remote to his imagination that it scarcely concerns him at all.

Most men attend their own funerals in their mind's eye at some time before they die, and foresee, not without pleasure, the effect of their deaths upon their relatives and friends (this is especially true of suicides and would-be suicides, for whom the emotional devastation, sometimes overestimated, wrought by their self-slaughter upon those who knew them in life is one of the act's principal consolations, if not motivations); but, in the absence of a culture of death, most men also know that, the funeral over, life will close over their memory like the earth over their coffins. We don't even bother any longer with the outward forms of bereavement: black is a colour of fashion nowadays rather than of mourning, and there are whole areas of cities – Camden Lock in London, for example – where the wearing of black is a symbol not of recent loss but rather of conscious inconformity to bourgeois society.

And disapprove as I might of this short way of dealing with death, I fully partake of it myself. More than once while driving I have been irritated by the slowness of a funeral cortège, as if death were not my destiny, as if the hold-up caused by the cortège were in the same category, say, as that caused by a football crowd going to a match which I was not going to attend and in which I had no interest.

Modern Man now lives in such vast agglomerations of people that, even without an appreciation of the size of the universe, his own insignificance is horribly clear to him. When he lived in a village from which he hardly ever strayed, within a very restricted circle which his imagination did nothing to expand, it was possible for him to delude himself about his individual importance; but now, when the majority of people live in conurbations incomparably larger than the largest cities in the world only half a millennium ago,* so that an excursion to a shopping centre is an exercise in anonymity, and when moreover electronic means of communication put him in mental touch with a pullulating world beyond his immediate ken, then he knows in his heart that he is more bacterium than Man, that he is made more in the image of *E. coli* than of God.

Modern Man knows in his bones, as no men have ever known before, that his life is the briefest of sparks in the darkest of darkness. It takes a stong mind to face this knowledge with equanimity, and most people do not have strong minds. That so much passion, so much striving, so much suffering should have gone into something as ephemeral and pointless as human existence is a bitter pill to swallow. No wonder, then, that modern Man seeks to prolong his life a little, for it is all he has. No wonder, also, that he reacts to any threat to his life, however remote, with fright – no, with existential terror. For what is even the longest life expectancy in recorded (or, for that matter, unrecorded) history, compared with the eternal dense black silence which awaits, whether you die at birth or live to receive the congratulatory telegram from the Queen on your hundredth birthday?

* Renaissance Florence had a population approximately one-third the size of contemporary Croydon.

XIX

But if Man is more bacterium than god, he is a bacterium endowed with certain inalienable rights, among them the right to life itself, of which right there could be no more complete negation than death. The Gulag Archipelago was not more a denial of the right to liberty than is death of the right to life. To change the biological metaphor, Man may be a worm, but he is a worm who has turned.

All men are created equal. By whom, or for what purpose, we treat as irrelevant by comparison with the great fact of equality itself. And in our own estimation, we are not levelled down, we are levelled up: every man his own Louis XIV. Our equality is not the existential equality of death, which is the subject of Richard II's great speech:

>   . . . for within the hollow crown
> That rounds the mortal temples of a king
> Keeps Death his court, and there the antick sits,
> Scoffing his state and grinning at his pomp;
> Allowing him a breath, a little scene,
> To monarchize, be fear'd and kill with looks,
> Infusing him with self and vain conceit
> As if this flesh which walls about our life
> Were brass impregnable; and humour'd thus
> Comes at the last, and with a little pin
> Bores through the castle wall, and farewell king!

On the contrary, we are the demigods of the beginning of Hamlet's soliloquy:

> What a piece of work is a man! How noble in reason! How infinite in faculty! in form, in moving, how express and admirable! in action how like an angel! in apprehension how like a god! the beauty of the world! the paragon of animals!

We choose to forget that even this noble being ends up, only one line later, as the quintessence of dust. No: not only are we the culmination of 3,500,000,000 years of evolutionary progress, from primaeval soup to the all-star cast of *Baywatch*, we are as important individually as anyone who ever lived. The tenet of equality guarantees this; and since some of the people who lived were clearly very important indeed, it follows that we must be very important also.

In the circumstances, therefore, death is a kind of outrage, a form of *lèse-majesté*. It is bad enough that we should sometimes be ill with curable diseases: we were not born for illness. It is vastly worse, however, that illnesses should exist which are incurable, becoming either chronic or fatal. And just as every absolute ruler who believes he has an indisputable or divine right to power institutes a system of espionage to root out those ill-intentioned persons who would destroy his power by questioning his right to exercise it, so our modern hypochondriacal Louis XIV spies out the threats to his immortality and grows alarmed by every indication that it is a snare and delusion. A man with pretensions – whether to imortality, to classical learning or to athletic prowess – is a frightened man, frightened lest his bluff be called and his pretensions exposed. The man who aspires to immortality and eternal youth – that is to say, modern Man – knows his aspiration to be impossible of attainment, knows that come what may or do what he will old age and death will come to him, yet pretends that he is on the verge of finding the elixir of life and that therefore his aspiration is not ridiculous and frivolous.* A man with pretensions worries away at them like a dog with an itch; and just as a coward is apt to provoke situations in which he hopes to demonstrate his bravery, so the aspirant to immortality cannot resist reports of new diseases and epidemics, as well as miracle cures.

Humility is no more fashionable a virtue these days than fortitude. For while fortitude is regarded as a species of emotional evasiveness, a dishonest refusal to face up to and express one's own true feelings, humility is regarded as the emotional hangover of an age of inequality and unjust social arrangements, according to which one man, an aristocrat, was regarded as intrinsically more important than another. But without either humility or fortitude, serenity is impossible, and every man is condemned to regard his own death as both catastrophic and avoidable. If every death, including his own, is avoidable, he must be as alert to risk factors as a herd of wildebeest must be to the presence of a lion. True, in a herd of ten thousand, the individual wildebeest's chances of being caught and eaten are remote indeed; but that does not stop him from running with the herd when it takes to the hoof. The difference between the wildebeest and the hypochondriac, of course, is that the wildebeest could – if granted the powers of speech – allude to the fact that it is precisely his willingness

---

* The medical correspondent of *The Economist*, Dr Alexandra Wyke, has just published a book predicting the final abolition of illness, thanks to the combined and additive effects of computer technology and genetic science.

to run with the herd which makes it unlikely that he will be eaten by the lion; whereas the hypochondriac who assiduously avoids the food additive E149, or inorganic tomatoes, has no such justification.

The human analogy to the wildebeest is, if he actually exists, the man with moderately raised blood pressure (a symptomless disease) who takes tablets daily in the hope of avoiding a stroke. On average, he would have to take them for 800 years to avoid a single stroke; or, to put it another way, 800 such people would have to take the pills for a year that a single stroke among them might be avoided; or (more realistically) eighty such hypertensives would have to take the pills for ten years each for one of them to avoid a stroke. What is almost certain is that only a very small proportion, if any at all, of our hypothetical hypertensives would have a better understanding of the basis on which they were taking their tablets than do the wildebeest for their policy of running with the herd. Incidentally, the man with moderately raised blood pressure does more for his health by taking pills to lower his blood pressure than does the man with moderately raised levels of cholesterol in his blood – by a factor of five or six.

It is undeniable, however, that the prospect of avoiding a stroke presents itself to our imagination with more emotional force and vigour than the prospect, many times more likely, of taking tablets to no purpose for decades, with the prospect of unpleasant side-effects thrown in for good measure. And in the absence of belief that life has any meaning beyond itself most of us are willing to go to considerable lengths and to make necessary sacrifices (as we imagine them) to obtain a stay of execution.

The more rights we bestow upon ourselves, and the more important we appear in our own eyes, the greater the insult death appears to us to be. No medical advance, short of that which will guarantee us immortality in a state of eternal youth, will rid us of our anxiety. The longer we live, in fact, and the more technological marvels we survive to witness, the greater grows our anxiety. We compare ourselves not with our ancestors, immediate or long dead, but with our lucky descendants. We adopt the rhetorician's trick of comparing the present not with the past, but with an ideal state still – allegedly – to come, in which death, unhappiness, inequality and bad weather will have been abolished. We want to play the role of the God we have lost:* He was immortal, why cannot we be?

XX

If anyone should be inclined to doubt that there is a connection between the search for perfect well-being and the consequent health scares on the one hand, and on the other a quest for transcendental meaning in an age of general unbelief, I recommend that he or she obtain a small publication called *South West Connection*. Published quarterly (and printed on environmentally friendly paper), it is subtitled *A guide to personal development and natural*

---

* The French philosopher, Auguste Comte, having abolished God by argumentation, even founded a cult in which Man formally worshipped himself. Fortunately, it did not catch on.

therapies. Its 112 pages list those alternative healers* who belong to what the editors call the Human Potential Movement, who practise their various arts in the south-west of England: an area of the country more than averagely populated, I suspect, by middle-class people of excellent life expectancy who, however, are not quite sure of the purpose of their existence.

One is spoilt for choice for evidence from this booklet in support of my thesis: every page yields its quota.

Why is the human race such a mess? asks one advertisement. 'Globally humans are rapidly destroying themselves, each other and the planet. Are you striving for community,' it asks again, but in different typeface, 'for personal and planetary harmony but can't get far enough despite therapies or spiritual practices? There is something fundamentally wrong that affects our whole physical, emotional and spiritual being. The simple bio-chemical clues are alarming and devastating, no wonder we're such a mess. For those really interested in fundamental exploration and change, contact. . .'

On the page opposite is an advertisement for Osho Leela, 'the Foundation for Joyous Living'.

Osho Leela is a community whose aim is to support all approaches and activities which help people discover their unique beauty and joy. We actively support the individual's liberation from fear, negative conditioning and feelings of powerlessness. . .

---

* The friend of mine, a general practitioner in London, who is kind enough to send me *South West Connection*, has established through his research that alternative medicine, so called, is not alternative: it's additional.

Treatments available at Osho Leela: Aromatherapy, Reiki, Breath, Reflexology, Hypnotherapy, Tibetan Pulsing, Cranio Sacral Balancing, Counselling, Tarot, Chakra Readings, Past Life Sessions.

As one reads on, the prophetic words of G. K. Chesterton come insistently to mind: when Man ceases to believe in God, he won't believe in nothing, he'll believe in anything. Here is some of what is on offer, chosen more or less at random.

A weekend at Portman Lodge with Diane Cooper promises Inner Peace on Saturday, while Sunday is devoted to Healing with Angels.

At the Rosehill Centre, 'we offer a range of holistic therapies and self-healing training and workshops in a tranquil environment combined with the opportunity to float in a unique flotation pool set in a sandstone grotto, the ultimate relaxation and preparation for therapy.'

The International Self-Realization Healing Association is 'for practitioners working for the development of unconditional love and spirituality with a high standard of healing practice'.

The Cosmic Force Centre (all major credit cards taken) offers: Reiki Healing daily by appointment, Reiki Sharing Circle last Thursday every month, Reiki Absent-Distant Healing service, upon request, for people – animals – situations, and Spiritual Pathway Tarot daily by appointment. The centre's shop sells, *inter alia*, over 2,000 Crystals and Minerals, Star Child Essential Oils, WindChimes, Talismans and Wild Colour Make-up and Hair Dye.

Valerie Reading teaches Channelling with the Ascended Masters: a powerful workshop which includes Realignment of the Etheric and Subtle Bodies to higher vibrations, Reactivation of cellular memory and Initiation by the Sword of the Archangel Michael, Alignment and overshadowing by the Masters facilitating an in-depth clearing of all emotional blockages (at very competitive prices).

Ambika Wauters (author of *Journey of Self-Discovery*, *Ambika Guide to Healing and Wholeness*, *The Angel Oracle* and *The Chakra Oracle*) runs a postgraduate training seminar for Mind/Body/Spirit Practitioners in the Human Energy System, which will develop your skills and expand your perception, teach you the bioenergetic character structures and how they affect our behaviour, attitudes and relationships, give you an understanding of how the chakras function and the emotional issues and archetypes connected to them, and you will experience colours, music, movement and massage as a means to decongest, release and rebalance the human energy system.

Allan Sweeney offers to help you become a Master Healer and a clear channel for the incredible healing energies of love. With his training, specially created in the sacred space of Shambhala, the Healing Heart of the Planet, you can expect profound personal, emotional and spiritual breakthroughs. Reiki is a Universal Life Energy in a gentle, powerful, healing art. Through a series of attunements your natural healing channel is awakened with an acceleration of physical, mental and emotional healing and spiritual growth. To be an effective healer your heart needs to be fully open, creating personal safety and spontaneous joy. You will increase your clairvoyance, clairaudience, clairsensience, knowing, and beingness for more effective healing. Recalling your previous lives as a healer will release past patterns and build your future confidence as a Master Healer. You will re-establish your connection to the Source of All That Is, to universal love and understanding, and you will learn to access your own Divine Guidance.

Just in case things go wrong, you can plan a meaningful, earth-friendly, DIY funeral, using an ecological cardboard coffin, plain and inexpensive or individually decorated.

Not, of course, that death is death: by no means. At the Tareth Centre, *Miracles Do Happen*, and the teaching focuses on the joyful message of a transcendent future for all. That is why there is so much emphasis on previous lives; for if one has had previous lives, the chances are that one will have future lives as well.

One can, by happy coincidence, simultaneously ascend to a higher spiritual plane and ward off the physical dangers attendant upon modern life: the Q*Link Pendant from Clarus Personal Energy Systems 'is a revolutionary new tool which *enhances* and strengthens your AURIC FIELD, facilitates links with *higher forces*, increases *energy* and *vitality*, enables *clear focus*, *wellbeing*, *mental clarity* and *mind/body balance*. Extensive scientific tests prove protection from man-made electromagnetic field radiations (EMF) from computers, mobile phones etc. The Q*Link is vital for Energy Workers, Practitioners, Healers, Therapists, Computer and Mobile Phone users, Athletes, Frequent Flyers and Anyone who wants more POSITIVE ENERGY in their lives.'

It is clear that – the technological sophistication of our society notwithstanding – one is not very far here from the mental world of the Nigerian healer, whose advertisement to the public (typical of the genre) I once wrote down in the city of Maiduguri:

Dr Nwatadibia Occult
Home of Wonders
Why Die in Silence?
For Your Spiritual Help, Such As, Witchcraft, Good Luck,
Pool-Secret, To Win Love, Magic Bird Pen, to Collect Debt,
Love, Talisman, Guard Against Poison, Cast Out Obanje,
Good Footballer and Employment,
We Can Also Make Impossible to Be Possible eg Barren
Women,
We Are the Indian Secret Agents in Talisman of All Kinds

The great difference between the Nigerian doctor (occult) and the healers who advertise in *South West Connection* is not in their methods, but in their clientele. Nigeria is a country in which life is still precarious, and obviously so. Not only do dead bodies appear regularly on the streets of Nigerian cities, but everyone accepts their appearance with remarkable equanimity, treating them merely as though they were ordinary obstructions in the roadway. It is possible still to starve to death in Nigeria, and according to the Civil Liberties Organisation of that country many prisoners each year do so, because the warders steal their food. The police are said to hire out their guns by the night to armed gangs; there are still public executions; and the hospitals are organised precisely as one might expect of such a country. Half the medicaments sold in the pharmacies are forgeries, the Nigerians having become highly expert (perhaps world-expert) in the production of pills and capsules which look precisely the same as *bona fide* drugs, but contain nothing but sand or chalk. The accident rate is probably the highest in the world, while many of the traditional curtailers of life are still rampant. Insecurity is everywhere.

The same can hardly be said of the south-west of England. The kind of security people seek there is of a different kind: not physical, but philosophical. They will never find it, because it isn't there to be found.

XXI

Health scares play an important part in the mental economy of modern Man. They allow him to believe that, were it not for this or that pollutant, he might be immortal, while explaining the anomaly of death. And they do something more: they provide him with that most indispensable of creatures, a scapegoat.

Almost all health scares have as a premise that someone is to blame for the alleged harm, in particular a political authority or the management of a vast corporation or cartel of corporations, as if the world, shorn of these nefarious men, would be perfectly safe, a Garden of Eden without the temptation which ruined things for us the first time round. We are dissatisfied with the limits imposed by Nature on our existence: we prefer to ascribe them to the human wickedness of others.

It goes without saying that the Common Man is blameless, for only those in authority, or with money and power, are free to act truly in accordance with their own will. That is why it is perfectly reasonable for smokers in the United States to sue the tobacco companies there, even though the harmful effects of consuming their products have been widely known and publicised for decades. (I have never met a smoker, be he illiterate or university professor, who did not know that smoking was bad for him.) The unfortunate smokers – common men all – were victims of the all-powerful tobacco companies, in whose hands we are all, or at least some of us, putty.

The smoker who blames the tobacco company (to be sure, in the hope of immense financial gain) for having taken tens of thousands of decisions over his lifetime to take a cigarette out of a packet, put it in his mouth, set it to smoulder and inhale the smoke, is not more childish than the six-year-old who imagines that adults in general are free to do anything they like, and his parents in particular are gods for whom all things are possible. But at least he has a satisfactory explanation for his lack of will-power in his struggle, if he has had one, to give up his habit, for his less than optimal health and for his foreshortened life. For as a common man, he can have done no wrong, have displayed no weakness, have suffered no random misfortune, have taken no foolish decisions, have engaged in no wilful self-destruction. Only the authorities have either the capacity or the inclination to act from ill will.

Needless to say, this is not a view to which I myself subscribe. I have little doubt of the ability of the authorities to act in accordance with the dictates of self-interest or evil, to lie, evade their responsibilities and all the rest of it, but my observations of the rest of humanity lead me to suppose that these are not faculties or traits which arise *de novo* in human beings only when they assume the mantle of power.

Few illusions are more comforting than that all the evil and dissolution in the world comes from without. Particularly is this so when we have lost faith that the universe is ordered according to a just, if for the moment inscrutable, purpose and plan, and that whatever hardship we may unjustly suffer in this life will be more than recompensed by a state of bliss elsewhere. Never are scapegoats more necessary than in an existence deprived of external meaning.

It remains, then, to design a health scare of our own. To be effective, our design should include the following features:

i) the threat should come from an item of consumption of ubiquitous distribution and universal use;

ii) the illness caused should not have bred contempt through familiarity, but on the contrary should be both rare and devastating enough to produce a *frisson* of fear in the middle classes;

iii) the producers of the threatening substance or product, and the government, should credibly (whether they were or not) have been involved in a conspiracy to withhold information from the public, thus permitting an outpouring of righteous indignation.

Is there any item of mass consumption which has not yet been the object of a recent scare? It should be borne in mind, of course, that no bill of health can ever be final, nothing can ever be declared safe once and for all, because future research might reveal what past research missed or failed to find. Still, for our purposes, it would be best to alight upon an item which until now has escaped suspicion; and I suggest tea.

It is indeed strange that this infusion of dried and fermented leaves, known to contain tannin and caffeine

among hundreds of other chemicals, which is of very wide
consumption, should have gone virtually unnoticed and
uncondemned by the epidemiologists and the health pages
of our newspapers. It is surely no coincidence that everyone
in Britain drinks tea, and that everyone there dies. Yes, tea-
drinkers have a death rate of 100 per cent! Research,
moreover, has demonstrated how dangerous a liquid tea is.

For example, when a few drops are added to the water
in a tank in which stickleback are breeding, a higher
percentage of their offspring than could be expected by
chance have a deformation. When the tails of white laboratory mice are immersed in cold tea for three months, 15
per cent of them develop cancer of the skin. When rabbits,
ferrets and guinea pigs are fed on a diet of tea through
nasogastric tubes, 7 per cent of them develop cancer of the
stomach. This experimental research, moreover, is
supported by epidemiological evidence: an examination of
the lives of 1,847 cases of cancer of the stomach demonstrated that 47 per cent of them had drunk more than five
cups of tea per day for twenty years, as against only 26 per
cent of those people, matched for age, sex, social class,
occupation, etc., who died of something else.

How is it that these facts have so far escaped public
notice? Is it not the case that tea is grown and marketed by
some of the largest food conglomerates in the country, if
not the world? We need look no further: the government,
besides raising import duty on tea, is in thrall to the multi-
nationals and dare not offend them. In short, it has actively
suppressed scientific findings, thereby sacrificing the
health of the population, to preserve commercial interests.
As for the tea-pickers of Assam and Sri Lanka, they would
be much better off without being exploited for their cheap
labour.

If tea were not drunk, we should all of us live on average thirty-seven minutes longer. Let us therefore forbid the advertising of tea, artistic portrayals (at least in a sympathetic light) of people taking tea, and the serving of tea in hospitals and other places of public resort. Let us demand appropriate health warnings on the packaging of tea, and higher taxes upon the noxious leaf to discourage consumption. Let us set up a Tea Educational Council, to inform people of the dangers of tea (it is addictive, after all!) and thereby employ several score of young graduates in psychology and sociology who are at a loose end, but who nevertheless feel an irresistible urge to serve the public. Let us aim to reduce national tea consumption by 40 per cent by the year 2013, and by even more among the specially vulnerable – for example, the old, the weak, the disadvantaged, the stressed, the tired, the unemployed, the depressed, the pregnant, the young, women, the middle-aged, the ill and the disabled.

XXII

Eat, drink and be merry, for you'll live to be eighty at least, which is a long time to worry over trifles.